£1-10

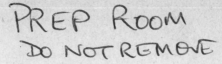

The Physics Laboratories

D0714608

Physics Teachers' guide **Unit 1**

Materials and structure

14 082701 3
Nuffield Advanced Science

Nuffield Advanced Physics team

Joint organizers

Dr P. J. Black, Reader in Crystal Physics, University of Birmingham

Jon Ogborn, Worcester College of Education; formerly of Roan School, London SE3

Team members

W. Bolton, formerly of High Wycombe College of Technology and Art

R. W. Fairbrother, Centre for Science Education, Chelsea College; formerly of Hinckley Grammar School

G. E. Foxcroft, Rugby School

Martin Harrap, formerly of Whitgift School, Croydon

Dr John Harris, Centre for Science Education, Chelsea College; formerly of Harvard Project Physics

Dr A. L. Mansell, Centre for Science Education, Chelsea College; formerly of Hatfield College of Technology

A. W. Trotter, North London Science Centre; formerly of Elliott School, Putney

Evaluation

P. R. Lawton, Garnett College, London

Acknowledgements

The organizers are grateful to the following for assistance in the preparation of Unit 1.

Dr J. E. Bailey

Professor R. G. Chambers

Dr A. Kelly

Professor P. L. Pratt

Professor E. H. Andrews

Dr B. Ralph

Mr A. G. Thomas

The first four named met as a working party on several occasions. All gave their time and energy freely, and they made many suggestions of material to incorporate. Much that is of value in Unit 1 came from them.

Physics Teachers' guide Unit 1
Materials and structure

Nuffield Advanced Science
Published for the Nuffield Foundation by Penguin Books

Penguin Books Ltd, Harmondsworth, Middlesex, England
Penguin Books Inc., 7110 Ambassador Road,
Baltimore, Md 21207, U.S.A.
Penguin Books Ltd, Ringwood, Victoria, Australia

Design and art direction by Ivan and Robin Dodd
Illustrations designed and produced by Penguin Education

Filmset in 'Monophoto' Univers
by Keyspools Ltd, Golborne, Lancs.
and made and printed in Great Britain
by Compton Printing Ltd, London and Aylesbury

Contents

Consultative Committee

Foreword

It is almost a decade since the Trustees of the Nuffield Foundation decided to sponsor curriculum development programmes in science. Over the past few years a succession of materials and aids appropriate to teaching and learning over a wide variety of age and ability ranges has been published. We hope that they may have made a small contribution to the renewal of the science curriculum which is currently so evident in the schools.

The strength of the development has unquestionably lain in the most valuable part that has been played in the work by practising teachers and the guidance and help that have been received from the consultative committees to each Project.

The stage has now been reached for the publication of materials suitable for Advanced courses in the sciences. In many ways the task has been a more difficult one to accomplish. The sixth form has received more than its fair share of study in recent years and there is now an increasing acceptance that an attempt should be made to preserve breadth in studies in the 16–19 year age range. This is no easy task in a system which by virtue of its pattern of tertiary education requires standards for the sixth form which in many other countries might well be found in first year university courses.

Advanced courses are therefore at once both a difficult and an interesting venture. They have been designed to be of value to teacher and student, be they in sixth forms or other forms of education in a similar age range. Furthermore, it is expected that teachers in universities, polytechnics, and colleges of education may find some of the ideas of value in their own work.

If the Advanced Physics course meets with the success and appreciation I believe it deserves, it will be in no small measure due to a very large number of people, in the team so ably led by Jon Ogborn and Dr Paul Black, in the consultative committee, and in the schools in which trials have been held. The programme could not have been brought to a successful conclusion without their help and that of the examination boards, local authorities, the universities, and the professional associations of science teachers.

Finally, the Project materials could not have reached successful publication without the expert assistance that has been received from William Anderson and his editorial staff in the Nuffield Science Publications Unit and from the editorial and production teams of Penguin Education.

K. W. Keohane
Co-ordinator of the Nuffield Foundation Science Teaching Project

The Teachers' guide

This volume is intended to contain whatever information and ideas are required for the day to day teaching of the Unit. Not every teacher will need all of it all of the time: sometimes the summary and the list of experiments will come nearer to meeting the need.

The main text contains, on the righthand pages, a detailed suggested teaching sequence, which teachers can adopt or adapt. The facing lefthand pages carry practical details, suggested questions, references, and background information for teachers in the form of a commentary on the text. This commentary also indicates aims of the teaching, and points out links with other parts of the course.

At the end, there are some appendices containing material needed on occasion only, and lists of apparatus and teaching aids for the Unit. These lists include details of books and articles referred to in this *Guide*.

Introduction

This Unit has been designed as an introductory Unit for the Advanced Physics course. We want the sixth form work to capture the students' imagination right from the beginning, and we choose for the first Unit a relatively complex topic which is of considerable practical importance but is treated simply.

The hope is that there will be quick rewards for students, and also that the Unit will illustrate some of the recurring issues of the course: arguments about models, understanding macroscopic behaviour in microscopic terms, and applying knowledge from one part of physics to tackle problems in another. Because gases were used to illustrate these issues in Nuffield O-level Physics, we turn back to solids.

Timing

The Unit is planned to be fairly brief, lest students become dismayed by the complexity of materials, and is intended to occupy not more than four weeks. A number of optional further areas for discussion are suggested. It is best *not* to use these unless there is interest and time can be found. It would be better to omit material than to run over the time suggested.

Aims

Detailed suggestions about what students should be expected to achieve appear in the commentary on lefthand pages. Overall, we hope to increase their awareness of the variety of materials, and to give them a (limited) knowledge of some important mechanical properties. Students should know that X-rays are used to investigate structures, and should have a first understanding of how this is done. Interference and diffraction will appear again in Unit 4, *Waves and oscillations*, and also in second year work on optics, in Unit 8, *Electromagnetic waves*, and in Unit 10, *Waves, particles, and atoms*.

We hope students will become more aware that the understanding of materials has a valuable role to play both in choosing materials for particular applications and in designing new materials. The strong 'applied' flavour of this Unit is deliberate.

Summary of Unit 1

Time: not more than four weeks.

(Numbers in brackets refer to suggested experiments, listed on page 5).

Part One
The variety and behaviour of materials

Time: not much over one double period.

This part is intended to give students experience of the behaviour of materials, out of which questions arise about the nature of materials. Some of the more detailed investigations of materials in Part Three (experiment 1.7) could be taken into Part One.

Suggested sequence

Handling useful materials (1.1), discussing how materials differ, discussing how they are used, and asking why they differ.

Part Two
X-rays and structure

Time: up to two weeks.

This part is about how X-rays can be used to discover the arrangement of atoms in a material, a question raised in Part One. A simple argument for one substance (copper) is suggested, using a microwave analogue of diffraction. Some indication of the scope of X-ray analysis as a tool in many fields can be given, and there is an opportunity to discuss the role of models in physics.

Suggested sequence

Revision — the sizes of atoms.

Bubble raft (1.2) and stacking spheres (1.3) to consider ways of stacking atoms.

Microwave analogue of X-ray diffraction (1.4).

Film loops of X-ray diffraction.

Bragg diffraction as a wave phenomenon, using microwaves (1.5, 1.6).

Structure of copper and size of a copper atom by scaling down microwave analogue results using X-ray data for copper.

The Avogadro constant.

Bragg's Law (could be taken later, in Units 4, 8, or 10). X-ray analysis as a tool widely used in many fields. Models in physics.

Part Three
Stretching and breaking

Time: up to two weeks.

This part links the observed abilities of materials to stretch, yield, and break, with ideas about the arrangement of atoms and the forces between atoms. Measuring the Young modulus and the breaking strength gives a chance to consider the design of a quantitative experiment, and to let students report their work to one another.

Measurements and observations can be interpreted in atomic terms, particularly by contrasting rubber, copper, and glass. Composite materials, such as fibreglass and reinforced concrete, can then be discussed as attempts to design new materials, using the insights into the limitations of materials gained previously.

Suggested sequence

Feeling materials stretch and break (1.7).

Measurements of the Young modulus and breaking strength (1.8) for rubber, steel, copper, glass, and, optionally, polythene. Terms: stress, strain, modulus, plastic, brittle, elastic. Force constant of an atomic bond.

More microscopic interpretation:
Rubber — orderliness of stretched rubber using X-rays, suggestion of molecules uncoiling (1.9).
Copper — bubble raft suggests dislocations as a slip mechanism in a regular structure (1.10).
Glass — disorderly structure, importance of cracks (1.11).

Composite materials (1.12). Research by students into literature on concrete, toughened glass, fibreglass, plywood, and wood, illustrating how materials engineers exploit the properties of materials to overcome their limitations.

Choosing one's own path

We hope and expect that teachers will find their own ways of using the material in this Unit. The detailed teaching programme laid out in the following pages represents as good a way of handling the material as we have been able to find in the light of experience in the trials, but should not be thought of as more than a possible, fairly well tested way of achieving the aims we decided upon. No doubt others can and will do better.

But teachers will know that it is the detail that counts in successful teaching, and so the *Guide* is full of particular teaching suggestions and practical details. We hope that these will help those who are uncertain how to handle either new material, or old material taught in a new way for unfamiliar aims.

The summary and list of experiments will, it is hoped, assist those who have taught the course a few times and no longer need to refer to all of the detailed teaching suggestions, as well as those who feel confident that they can make up their own teaching programme out of their previous experience. We also hope that the summary will provide an overall view of the work suggested. Such a view is necessary for keeping a sense of perspective and direction, both when one is immersed in particular detailed teaching suggestions and comments, and when students lead the teaching off in an unpredictable direction by contributing their own ideas.

It seems fair to add that the summary, taken on its own, could mislead. It cannot easily indicate the aims of pieces of work in any precise way, or find words to express the relative seriousness or lightness of particular episodes. Nor should a phrase one might find in a current examination syllabus always be taken here to imply the same work as it would imply there.

Experiments suggested for Unit 1

The variety and behaviour of materials

Time: not much over one double period

Purpose and timing

Part One starts the Unit off from the point of view of the application of materials, as Part Two, about X-ray diffraction, may seem to have too 'pure' a bias. It need not last more than a double period. Teachers may like to extend it by taking some of the qualitative stretching and breaking experiments from Part Three, experiment 1.7. In trials, some classes benefited from such a broader experience of the behaviour of materials, while others found it too childish for the start of the Advanced course.

Other introductions

Waves

Part Two will assume some acquaintance with interference as a wave property, and for some classes it may be well to begin with ripple tank work (see Nuffield O-level *Teachers' guide III*, pages 122–39), explaining that soon they will be seeing how the waves called X-rays are used to study the structure of materials.

Bridge building contest

The American E.C.C.P. project, 'The man-made world', suggests that groups of students should compete to build the strongest bridge that will span a given distance, say 20 cm. Each group has the same amount of balsa wood (say 2 to 3 mm sticks), glue, and pins. A group needs several metres of wood.

The contest could give scope for imagination, good guesswork, and know-how, and should give occasion to introduce concepts such as stress and strain, when the bridges are compared. But it will not suit all students, and it may not be easy to link it with the rest of the Unit. Nor was it part of the trials course.

Experiment
1.1 Handling useful materials

Selection such as:

1054	stainless steel wire, 1 m lengths, 44 s.w.g. bare (item 7A may serve)
2B	copper wire, 1 m lengths, 32 s.w.g. bare
1054	glass rod, 0.1 m lengths, about 3 mm diameter (soda glass)
1053	glass wool, such as that used for insulating roofs
1053	glass fabric, such as that sold for curtains
1053	nylon fishing line, 1 m lengths
1053	rubber bands, at least 50 mm long
1053	plywood: samples of 3-ply and 5-ply in squares or strips big enough to bend
1053	fibreglass: sample pieces if available
1053	polythene: food bags, other polythene sacks, heavy gauge sheet sold for gardening
1053	plastics: lunch boxes (item 100/1) are common, and if made of polystyrene can be compared with expanded polystyrene; plastic roofing material can be obtained
1053	concrete: ready mixed cement and aggregate from builders' merchants cast in short bars in cardboard or hardboard moulds; allow at least 24 hours for setting
1053	wood: soft and hard wood; balsa wood, chipboard, and blockboard could be added
1053	paper: especially corrugated paper used for packaging

Part One is about the widely varying properties of materials, and the uses to which they may be put.

It also asks why a material should behave as it does; much of the rest of the Unit explores a few answers to such questions. Understanding why a material has its special properties could assist a scientist to design new and better materials. A physicist might learn much about forces between atoms from such a study.

Experiment
1.1 Handling useful materials

Have available samples of many materials, choosing generally those which are used for their strength.

We suggest things made of materials such as:

steel

copper

possibly other metals, including bars or rods

glass rod and woven glass cloth

nylon thread or fishing line

rubber

plywood

fibreglass

polythene, plastics

concrete

wood

corrugated paper

and any other materials of interest as they become available, for example, carbon fibre reinforced materials.

Ask the questions, 'What is it?' 'What is it made of?' 'What is it used for?' 'Why might it be suitable for that use?'

Encourage students to pull or bend specimens, asking them to describe what they feel. It may be useful to encourage them to pull, release, pull harder, and so on, so that elastic behaviour is observed.

It may be desirable to extend this into further qualitative stretching experiments, as in Part Three, experiment 1.7.

Reading

Gordon, *The new science of strong materials,* should be available. Give it to someone to take home, or ask a student to find the answer to a problem in it. Chapter 4, for example, is about why materials break.

Loftas and Gwynne, *Advances in materials science*, was recommended to us by a trials student.

See also Clarke, 'Materials and their uses', in the *Students' book.*

For details of reading recommended in this Commentary, see the list entitled 'Books and further reading' on page 105.

Discussion

The overall aims of the course discussed in the *Teachers' handbook* call for several kinds of ability. One is the ability to talk sense about physical problems. Another expects students to learn that argument and discussion are essential components of scientific inquiry, and to experience some of the most important kinds of argument. Other aims also imply a developing ability to talk, or will be helped if students have enjoyed being involved in talking about problems. Above all, then, the course should start in such a way that students see that discussion is both valued and expected. Teachers will need to encourage contributions — asking individuals to tell the rest about fibreglass, fishing line, concrete, or plywood. Too many contributions from the teacher could spoil this atmosphere. Students are not expected to memorize what they see, but to think of things to observe and describe.

The outcome of the discussion should not be information, but awareness that it is sensible to think about such matters. Students should come to expect to be asked questions of this kind.

Students' book

See questions 1–7.

Questions 1, 2, or 3 could be used with experiment 1.1. Questions 4 and 5 may introduce words such as 'elastic', 'plastic', 'strong', 'tough', or 'brittle', making a useful expansion of vocabulary. Question 7 may serve later for revision, while question 6 is a speculative exercise.

The history of materials

The broader social significance of the availability of materials with various properties might be brought out by a little history. For example:

Stone age — hard, brittle material.

Bronze age — hard, tough material, somewhat ductile.

Iron age — hard, tough, ductile material, cheap.

More recently:
steel — less brittle and stronger than iron.

plastics ⎫
⎬ — new possibilities.
composites ⎭

Discussion – the choice of material

Before, after, or together with the handling of materials, one can pose some problems about their uses. One or two like the following may suffice:

> What materials are used in cars? Why is each chosen for its job? Could others be used? (Fibreglass.)
>
> What different materials have been used for frying pans? (Cast iron, steel, copper, glass, ceramics.) What advantages or disadvantages does each have?
>
> What materials are used for wrapping and tying things? (Paper, cord, polythene, string, steel bands, etc.) What decides the choice?
>
> How are things fixed together? (Glues, nuts and bolts, screws, rivets.)

Speculation about the future will provide an opportunity to focus attention for a while on the composite and sandwich materials, and to mention that there will be a closer look at composite materials at the end of this Unit.

What decides how a material behaves?

When pulled or bent, copper yields, glass snaps, and rubber stretches a long way but recovers. Some brief speculation may be encouraged: how might the atoms or molecules differ, or how might their arrangement inside the materials differ to produce such variations? Raising the question introduces Part Two which studies evidence about the arrangement of atoms and molecules in materials.

Part Two

X-rays and structure

Time: up to two weeks.

Looking ahead

In later work ('Ionic crystals') in Unit 3, *Field and potential*, and in Unit 9, *Change and chance*, the ideas from this Part about the regular arrangement of atoms in a crystal will be needed, and similar ideas will be used in other places from time to time. Unit 8, *Electromagnetic waves*, will use and develop diffraction ideas, and electron diffraction will find an important place in the final Unit, *Waves, particles, and atoms.*

Bragg's Law

Bragg's Law for X-ray diffraction is developed here, for use in Unit 10, *Waves, particles, and atoms*. But the Law follows after simpler arguments, and could be postponed if necessary. Many students in the trials have, on the other hand, expressed pleasure at meeting a definite, clear piece of physics at this point.

The simple arguments, to precede Bragg's Law, use a model crystal built of large spheres which is used in a beam of 3 cm microwaves as an analogue of X-ray diffraction. The spheres are chosen to have a diameter such that the analogue is a scaled-up version of the diffraction of 0.154 nm X-rays by copper, so that the diffraction angles are equal in the two cases, and the size of a copper atom can be obtained by scaling down the analogue in the ratio of the two wavelengths.

Order of treatment

This guide for Part Two offers a simple treatment of X-rays and the structure of solids. We think it has merits, but no doubt teachers will adapt its order to their own ideas and needs. There should be, however, no need to introduce further ideas, such as descriptions of other crystal lattices, rotation or Laue X-ray photography, or a highly rigorous treatment of Bragg's Law.

The Avogadro constant

This constant appears in both the Nuffield O-level Physics and Chemistry courses. Students who need help in using it can be referred to the Nuffield Advanced Chemistry programmed text, *Amount of substance, the mole concept and its use in solving problems.* They need only use Section A, Chapter 1.

Students' book

See questions 8 to 11. Questions 8 to 10 practise the use of the mole concept and the Avogadro constant. Question 11 is an estimating question: it and others like it are worth using from time to time.

Handling large and small numbers

Students find numbers such as 10^{23}, 10^{-10}, 10^{-19} hard to manage, but the best way to learn to use them is to use them. There are many occasions in the course, such as the questions above, when short calculations using such numbers appear. Students need to be told that they are expected — gradually — to become able to handle them and to recognize the order of magnitude of the quantities involved. It is necessary to have an idea of these orders of magnitude in order to be able to think sensibly about problems on the microscopic scale.

How big is an atom?

Part One ended with questions about the arrangement of atoms in a material. A start can be made by looking back at ideas from O-level.

How big is an atom?

The investigation using an oil film from Nuffield O-level Physics, *Guide to experiments I* (class experiment 68) and the investigation of the kinetic theory in *Teachers' guide IV* yielded much information:

length of an olive oil molecule	about 16×10^{-10} m
diameter of a carbon atom	about 1.3×10^{-10} m
diameter of a molecule of 'air'	about 4×10^{-10} m
Avogadro constant	about 6×10^{23} mol^{-1}

The Avogadro constant can be obtained from the size of an atom, and such a calculation will come later (page 41). The principle is simple enough. One mole of atoms is chosen to be the number of atoms in exactly 12 g of ^{12}C. The size of a carbon atom can be used to work out how many atoms fit into any particular volume of solid carbon, as long as the way the atoms go together and how much space there is between them is known. Then if the volume chosen is the measured volume of 12 g of carbon, the number of atoms is the Avogadro constant. Actually, we shall use copper, not carbon, and rely on the chemical knowledge that 63.6 g of copper contains as many atoms as 12 g of carbon.

For such reasons, as well as for its inherent interest and possible practical value, the next matter considered is the problem of finding out how atoms are arranged in solids.

What would be a sensible substance to choose about which to ask the question, 'How are the atoms arranged?' Rubber, plastics, wood, or concrete are rather complicated chemically; it would be best to start with a substance containing just one kind of atom only. Copper is a common and useful pure substance, and we consider that first.

Information for teachers

The atoms of copper take up a face-centred cubic arrangement.

Figure 1
Unit cell of face-centred cubic arrangement.

Figure 1 shows the cubical unit which, repeating indefinitely in all directions, makes up the structure. An atom appears at the centre of each face of this 'unit cell'. If the atoms are spheres in contact, they occupy 74 per cent of the space, which is the most efficient possible packing in a regular three-dimensional structure. See Appendix A for more details.

Demonstration
1.2 A raft of equal sized bubbles

100/1	rectangular plastic tank
	or
90/A	ripple tank without legs
1055	length of rubber tubing to fit gas tap
1054	glass tube to fit into rubber tubing and drawn out to a fine jet at the other end
	or
1055	hypodermic needle, 25 gauge
1056	Teepol or washing-up liquid
1056	glycerol
522	Hoffmann clip

Recipes

A little washing-up liquid in water. More elaborate: Teepol, glycerol, water, in the proportion 1:8:32 parts by volume.
Bubbles are blown by connecting the jet to the gas tap. The clip is used to adjust the rate of flow of gas.

The packing together of copper atoms

Atoms of copper are all alike. They must be attracted to each other, otherwise the material would not hold together, but there must also be some force which prevents them from getting too close. Soap bubbles exhibit these properties. With care they can all be made the same size; surface tension pulls them together and at the same time the pressure inside prevents them from getting too close.

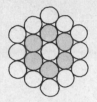

Figure 2
Atoms packed as closely as possible in a layer.

Demonstration
1.2 A raft of equal sized bubbles

The bubble raft shows that the bubbles cling together in an ordered manner, each one having six others around it. See figure 2. When a lot of bubbles are formed there may be discontinuities (grain boundaries) where one collection of ordered bubbles does not quite fit with another collection. The close-packed arrangement taken up by bubbles in a bubble raft is shown in figure 3.

Figure 3
Bubble raft.
Photograph, Sir Lawrence Bragg, F.R.S.

There may also be defects such as an occasional bubble which is a different size, or a space where a bubble is missing. All these are relevant to the study of materials and more will be said about them later. For the moment, however, the main point is that the bubbles pack as shown in figure 3.

The bubbles form into an orderly arrangement in two dimensions. What might an orderly arrangement of atoms in three dimensions look like?

A raft of equal-sized bubbles packs together into a layer with each bubble as close as possible to its neighbours, in a hexagonal arrangement. An image of the raft can be projected using an overhead projector, or a larger raft can be made in a ripple tank. The size of the bubbles formed for a given rate of flow of gas depends on the size of the jet and the depth it is held below the surface of the solution. It is best to start with a very fine jet and break pieces off the end until it gives satisfactory results. A 25 gauge hypodermic needle works well. When a satisfactory depth has been found, the jet should be clamped into position in one corner of the tank and the bubbles swept with a microscope slide into the body of the tank as they are formed. Wrongly sized bubbles can be burst with a hot wire and the whole raft can be cleared by playing a Bunsen burner over it.

The bubble raft can be shown very quickly – a visual impression is the most useful result.

Slide

Slide 1.16 shows a raft with 'grain boundaries'.

Demonstration
1.3 Stacking spheres

1016/2   expanded polystyrene sphere, 50 mm diameter   *40*

Books *or*
wood battens, 0.25 m long   *4*

This model is built because it happens to have the same (face-centred cubic) structure as copper. Oranges might be used in place of expanded polystyrene spheres.

Lay out a square 5 × 4 ball array inside a 0.25 × 0.2 m fence, and pile further balls on top in places such as X, figure 4. The stack is shown in figure 6.

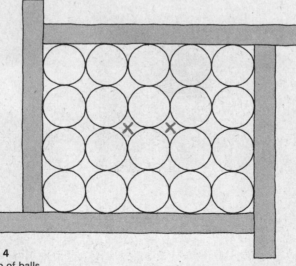

Figure 4
Starting off a heap of balls.

Demonstration
1.3 Stacking spheres

Greengrocers make orderly stacks of oranges for display. They often start with a
'layer of fours' in a 'square pattern' as in figure 5.

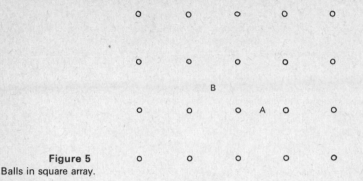

Figure 5
Balls in square array.

Having set out such a layer, where can the first orange of the next layer be put? It
may roll off in any direction if put vertically above an orange in the first layer. It may
roll off in either of two directions if put at A, but it stays firm at B.

Second, third, and fourth layers of twelve, six, and two balls can now be piled on
the first. When physicists talk of 'structures', they mean tidy heaps. This is one
possible kind of tidy heap.

Notice that the sloping sides have balls closely packed in hexagonal array (figure 6),
a 'layer of sixes' like the soap bubbles. Is this heap made of 'square' or
'hexagonal' layers? (Both, depending on how one chooses to look at it.)

Figure 6
A heap of balls or oranges.

See questions 12 to 16. Questions 12 and 13 follow up the soap bubble analogy. Question 14 may be useful in class discussion. Questions 15 and 16 produce a value of the Avogadro constant from experimental results. They could be saved until later (see page 41).

Tactics

This brief stacking exercise, recalling O-level work, serves to introduce the meaning of 'structure'. It should also lead students to look for a variety of regular layers in a regular structure, which will be useful when they come to think about the effect of such a structure upon a beam of waves in the next experiment.

In the microwave analogue of X-ray diffraction which follows, these layers will each give a strong 'reflection' at a characteristic angle. These angles will be used to suggest that copper atoms might be stacked in the same pattern, when it is found that copper diffracts X-rays of suitable wavelength at these same angles.

Note

Instructions for building the face-centred cubic 'crystal' of polystyrene spheres appear in Appendix B.

A large model crystal

A large model, of two hundred expanded polystyrene balls, each 50 mm in diameter, stuck together, can now be produced and the question can be asked, 'Has it the same structure?' (It has.) The model has been built up differently in the sense that it started from a hexagonal layer and then similar layers were stuck on. Because each layer was of the densest sort (in balls per unit area) and because the layers have been packed together as closely as possible, it will seem reasonable that no other structure could be more closely packed (in balls per unit volume).

Students are not required to remember the layers and their arrangements, but they will need to know that there are regular layers of more than one sort ('fours' and 'sixes').

Figure 7
Large model crystal.

Preparation for microwave analogue experiment

How might one discover if the atoms of, say, copper are or are not arranged in this or in some other proposed fashion? Can one look and see? Why not?

The use of very short waves such as X-rays may be suggested, or may have to be offered. (Nuffield O-level Chemistry refers to X-ray diffraction.) X-rays are nowadays widely used to investigate the structure of materials.

X-ray film loops

Four 8 mm loops have been made in conjunction with the project. Details appear on page 100.

Note that the first loop shows, at the end, X-rays detected by a Geiger counter at a low enough intensity for the randomness of arrival of photons to show up. This is an opportunity to mention, in passing, an idea which will be increasingly important in the course, especially towards the end.

Demonstration
1.4 Microwave diffraction by a polystyrene ball 'crystal'

184/1/2   3 cm wave transmitter, receiver, and power pack

181   general purpose amplifier
and

183   loudspeaker

1015   turntable, for 3 cm X-ray diffraction analogue

1014   wax lens   *2*

1053   metal screen, about 0.3 m square

59   l.t. variable voltage supply

64   oscilloscope

1016   polystyrene sphere, crystal model (see Appendix B)

1000   leads

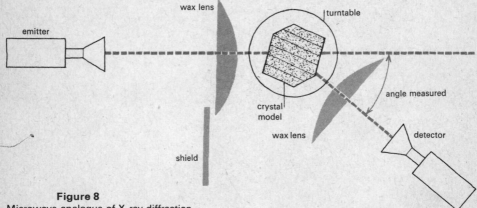

Figure 8
Microwave analogue of X-ray diffraction.

Figure 8 shows the arrangement of the apparatus. The transmitter and receiver are placed on stands so that they are at the same height as the centre of the model which rests on the turntable with its unfinished face downwards, as in figure 7. The waves are made roughly horizontal and parallel by a convex wax lens 9 or 10 wavelengths in diameter. The focus of the lens is not easy to find accurately, but the emitter should be placed at such a distance from the lens as to produce the most nearly parallel beam of radiation. The turntable should be well below the beam, and may rotate at 50 r.p.m. The detector, placed at the focus of a second lens and mounted so they move together, swings to various angles on both sides of the incident beam. There should be some simple means of measuring the angles. The scattered beams have much less intensity than the incident beam and

Film loops of X-ray work

Some teachers may wish to precede the microwave analogue of X-ray diffraction by a glimpse of the real thing on film; others may prefer to show the loops after the analogue experiment, when students will have more idea of what they could expect to see.

The first film loop shows an X-ray apparatus, and the use of a Geiger counter and ratemeter to detect the beam.

The second film loop shows X-rays (wavelength 0.154 nm) being diffracted by a single crystal of sodium chloride. The crystal, which most students should be prepared to regard as a regular stack of atoms (ions, strictly speaking), 'reflects' the beam at certain very definite angles, and only at these angles.

A large scale analogue experiment may now be offered, as a way of exploring the puzzling behaviour of the X-rays. If the X-ray loops (page 35) are not used, the use of the analogue follows directly upon the suggestion that radiation of appropriate wavelength shone upon a structure might help one to find out how it is built up.

Demonstration
1.4 Microwave diffraction by a polystyrene ball 'crystal'

The class can now see what happens when the large crystal model is placed in a beam of microwaves. If students have not been shown the X-ray films they can be told that the structures of materials like salt, copper, or polythene are investigated in a similar way using the short waves called X-rays.

If the model is not on the turntable, a signal is only heard when the detector is in line with the emitter. With the model rotating on the table, a signal is detected as the detector is swung round to an angle of about 44°, the gain of the amplifier being turned up.

Listening to the signal at its loudest, in each revolution the class will hear two pairs of loud 'bleeps' separated by longer than the time between a pair (figure 9).

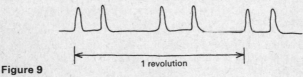

Figure 9
Signal at 44° (reflections from hexagonal layers).

It seems as if microwaves are being 'reflected' into the detector at this angle. (Here the use of the word 'reflected' will naturally prompt students to look for reflecting surfaces or layers in appropriate positions.)

therefore scattering by gas taps, teachers, and students, must be avoided. At some collimator angles a metal shield may be needed to stop radiation passing direct from emitter to detector. The detector is connected to an amplifier and loud speaker, the emitted waves being modulated at an audio frequency. Some may find it easier to detect a maximum if the amplified signal is fed into an oscilloscope with its time-base switched off.

The experiment is not an easy one and needs care and practice.

It is easier to detect the effect of the crystal on the microwaves, but less easy to measure the angles, if the transmitter and receiver are both placed about two metres from the rotating 'crystal'. The apparatus can be set out on three tables, suitably positioned. No wax lens need be placed in front of the receiver, but the transmitter should be at the focal point of a wax lens placed between it and the crystal. In this variation, it is best to use a portable battery-powered amplifier connected to the receiver.

Timing

There is no sense in rushing demonstration 1.4, especially if that would cut short discussion about what is happening.

Diffraction angle and layer spacing (note for teachers)

By starting at the smallest angles, Bragg reflections are first found from those layers which are most widely spaced, since $\lambda = 2d \sin \theta$, d being the layer spacing. Such layers must be those which are most closely packed within themselves, that is, the 'hexagonal' layers.

At larger angles, reflections from layers which are less closely packed within themselves – like the 'square' ones – and so are closer together in the crystal are obtained.

Preliminary revision?

Three-dimensional diffraction is not a situation students will readily understand. Demonstration 1.5 is about the wave properties of the microwave radiation, and some teachers will prefer to show it first. Unless the class knows little about waves, we prefer the order suggested because it raises questions and shows why the wave experiments of 1.5 may be needed. The diffraction experiment 1.4 should indicate how much revision is needed.

Theory before experiment?

It might seem more 'logical' to discuss the Bragg equation first, and then do experiment 1.4, and that would be best if the sole aim were to convince students of the truth of the Bragg equation and of its use in analysing the experiment. But there are other aims, particularly to practise thinking about a new problem using ideas from earlier work and to show how theoretical ideas are developed in physics to explain new and puzzling results. So we suggest doing it by meeting some experimental facts first and thinking about making sense of them.

The demonstration is arranged so that useful answers can be obtained without the Bragg equation, and students can then see what kind of ideas are being used, shorn of theoretical complications. Some could leave the matter there, though most can go on to discuss the Bragg equation $\lambda = 2d \sin \theta$. This choice is discussed later.

At least the experiment and simple argument will show students why the Bragg argument considers the effect of layers of atoms on waves.

Can the class see any layers which might be responsible? Fortunately, the right layers are the most obvious ones; that is, the 'hexagonal' layers, a pair of which lie in a vertical plane and can easily be seen in figure 7. There is a pair of reflections as first one layer and then the other bisects the angle between the beam and the detector, and then a second pair after the 'crystal' has rotated through 180° to bring the backs of these layers into line (figure 10). It is convenient to rotate the crystal by hand.

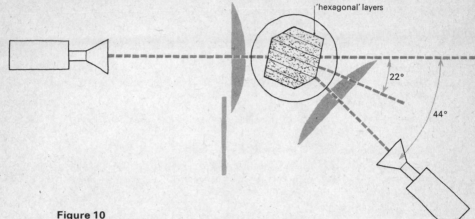

'hexagonal' layers

22°

44°

Figure 10
Microwave diffraction; the 44° reflections.

Microwaves are strongly reflected from these layers when they strike them at 22°, being turned through 44°. Why? Before taking up that problem, try larger angles. At 50° (microwaves incident at 25°) there is another strong reflection, but with two 'bleeps' per revolution (figure 11). These come from the 'square' layers.

At larger angles, after these closely spaced reflections at 44° and 50°, there is nothing regular until an angle of 74° is reached, when a third reflection can be heard. This too has two maxima per revolution (also as in figure 11).

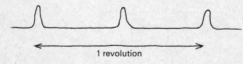

1 revolution

Figure 11
Signal at 50° (reflections from 'square' layers).

The class may wish to look for layers responsible for the reflection at 74°, but it will probably be best if they remain content with noting the three angles, having identified layers associated with the first two.

Later use of the observations

The pattern of 'two reflections close together and a third further round' is one that will later be recognized in X-ray photographs of copper. Students need not remember the angles after they have been used in this way but should recall that regularly spaced layers give strong 'reflections' at definite angles.

Film loops of X-ray diffraction

The two loops mentioned on page 22, may be shown now if they were not shown then, illustrating here how X-rays are 'reflected' from a sodium chloride crystal in a way similar to the 'reflection' of microwaves from the model.

Reading

The Nuffield Chemistry background booklet *The start of X-ray analysis* by Sir Lawrence Bragg may be offered for reading. Perhaps one student could prepare to tell the others about it when the next X-ray film loops are shown and the structure of copper emerges.

The *Scientific American* offprint 'X-ray crystallography' by Sir Lawrence Bragg is also valuable.

Bragg planes (note for teachers)

In the crystal model the planes which decide the direction of the Bragg reflections are planes of atoms. They need not be, in general. The three-dimensional repeating structure may be built of more complex units, such as groups of atoms or molecules.

If each ball in the model were replaced by some unsymmetrical object representing a complex molecule, the model would have the same planes and would reflect in the same directions. But the intensity of the reflections in particular directions would be altered, since the unsymmetrical objects will be orientated to scatter more in some directions than in others.

Simple diffraction gratings behave similarly. The spacing of the slits is all that decides the directions of diffraction maxima, but the exact shape of the slits – width, depth of ruling, profile, etc – determines the intensities of the various maxima.

In X-ray studies, the intensities of the diffraction pattern give information about the grouping of atoms within whatever unit it is that repeats in three dimensions. The directions of the diffraction maxima give information about the pattern in which this unit repeats in space, but not about the nature or symmetry of the repeat unit itself.

Optional – layers responsible for the 74° reflection

Return to the heap of balls built in demonstration 1.3 and build another, but with a glass or Perspex plate in a vertical plane parallel to one of the edges of the 'square' base array. See figure 12.

rows of balls making one layer

Figure 12
Layer responsible for 74° reflection.

Against the plate, there lie horizontal rows of balls; the balls of each row touch, but the rows are separated by gaps. The rows of balls in the next layer of this kind fit into the gaps between the rows in the front layer.

The unfinished base of the crystal model (figure 7) is a layer of this kind.

These layers lie in planes at right angles to the hexagonal, closely packed layers in the sloping sides of the heap, and so at right angles to similar layers in the large crystal model.

Demonstration (for discussion)
1.5 **Microwaves**

184/1/2 3 cm wave apparatus (transmitter, receiver, and power supply)

181 general purpose amplifier
and

183 loudspeaker

1053 metal reflector, about 0.3 m square

1053 hardboard partial reflector, about 0.3 m square

1014 wax lenses

1000 leads

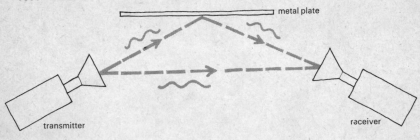

Figure 13
'Lloyd's mirror' with microwaves.

Both meter indication and audible indication may be used. For the latter, the microwaves must be modulated. The simplest 'wave' experiment is probably 'Lloyd's mirror' (figure 13).

If the receiver catches waves from the transmitter both directly and after reflection, interference effects are observed when the path difference is changed either by moving the reflecting metal plate or the receiver.

Pace

It would be easy to get into a long exposition or piece of revision here, but that would be a mistake. There will be plenty of time later in the course to look long and carefully at wave behaviour (Unit 4).

The purpose of demonstrations 1.5 and 1.6 is to suggest that the 'reflections' observed from the model crystal might be explained as the result of interference between waves scattered from layers, without going into any detailed theory at this stage.

Students' book

See questions 17, 18, 19.

Demonstration (for discussion)
1.5 Microwaves

Students who have never seen the microwave apparatus need to be shown what microwaves will do, and to have some evidence that they are waves. It may be best to ask individual students how they would demonstrate some of the following points:

1   The transmitter sends out a beam in front of it.

2   The signal becomes weaker at bigger distances.

3   Whether the beam goes through a hand, a metal sheet, or a hardboard sheet.

4   Whether a metal or hardboard sheet reflects the beam (check the angles).

5   The wax lenses will focus the beam.

Can the class suggest experiments to test whether the radiation is really wavelike?

Demonstration
1.6 Bragg 'reflection' of microwaves

184/1/2 3 cm wave apparatus

1015 turntable for 3 cm X-ray diffraction analogue

59 l.t. variable voltage supply for turntable

1014 wax lens   *2*

181 general purpose amplifier
and
183 loudspeaker

1053 sheet of expanded polystyrene, about 0.3 m square (e.g. ceiling tile)   *2*

1053 sheet of expanded polystyrene arranged parallel with 30 mm spacers   *12*

1053 metal screen, about 0.3 m square

1053 glue, which does not dissolve the tiles (Evo-stik 863)

1000 leads

plane layer of 50 mm spheres (optional)

The centres of the tiles should be about 30 mm apart. This value of 30 mm (about the wavelength of the microwaves) makes θ in the Bragg equation 30°. Since the beam turns through twice this angle the detector has to be placed at an angle of 60° from the straight-through position.

The microwave apparatus and turntable from 1.4 is used, with the tiles in a vertical plane on the turntable.

Some expanded polystyrene tiles are not dense enough to reflect much radiation when a single tile is used. Sheets of hardboard can be used instead.

Film loops (optional)

Ealing Scientific 'Bragg reflection of waves', shows how an array of scattering centres in a ripple tank can give maxima at definite angles. The Longman loop 'The diffraction of X-rays by a crystal' is similar. See page 100 for a list of loops.

Demonstration
1.6 Bragg 'reflection' of microwaves

Having arranged a single polystyrene tile to reflect the parallel beam through a lens to the receiver, bring a second tile up behind the first and parallel to it. Rises and falls in intensity occur, as the extra path to the second tile is either an even or odd number of half wavelengths.

Some may like to show that a glued-up flat layer of balls reflects just like a flat tile. Students are not likely to appreciate arguments either that this might be in doubt, or that it ought to be so. (See page 44.)

The single tile would reflect at any angle. Now use an array of 12 tiles, all equally spaced (figure 14).

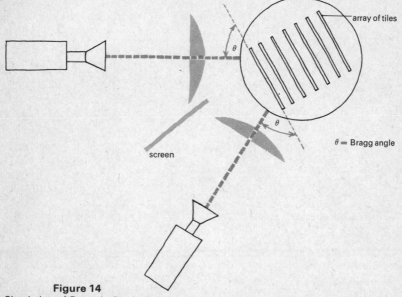

Figure 14
Simulation of Bragg 'reflection' with a stack of tiles.

These will reflect the beam, but only at definite angles. There is little reflection at other angles even though the planes are correctly placed, halving the angle between beam and detector.

Visits to see real X-ray diffraction experiments

Most universities and some technical colleges have X-ray diffraction apparatus. It would be best to ask to see powder photography.

Ideally, a powder photograph using a copper wire would be taken, and the class supplied with prints.

The type of educational X-ray apparatus used in the film loops is too expensive for a school, but might be afforded by an LEA for loan to schools. Such apparatus may also be found in teaching laboratories of some universities or colleges in the future.

The general picture (figure 15) is of a wave coming in, and many bits of wave coming off each layer, adding up to a big reflection when the extra path along which the wave goes between layers is just right.

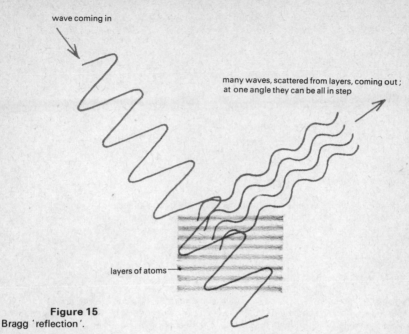

wave coming in

many waves, scattered from layers, coming out; at one angle they can be all in step

layers of atoms

Figure 15
Bragg 'reflection'.

The experiments with microwaves make it seem that we have to do with an interference effect resulting from path differences between layers.

The second film loop which students will have seen by now (page 22 or 26) shows X-rays reflected at a definite angle from a crystal of salt. Perhaps the microwave experiments are similar, but on a bigger scale. It would be well to look more closely at the diffraction of X-rays by crystals.

Film loops of X-ray diffraction

See page 100 for a list of loops. The loops *(1)* 'Production of the X-ray beam' and *(2)* 'Diffraction of monochromatic X-rays by a single crystal' will probably already have been shown. The third loop, 'Diffraction of monochromatic X-rays by a powder specimen', develops the idea of powder photography. The fourth loop, 'Determination of the wavelength of X-rays using a diffraction grating', shows how X-ray wavelengths may be measured.

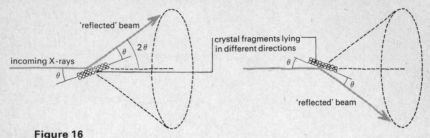

Figure 16
Cones of X-rays diffracted by small crystals.

The cones (figure 16) show all possible directions for X-ray beams reflected by small crystals which happen to lie with planes at an angle θ to the incoming beam, these planes having spacing d in $\lambda = 2d \sin \theta$.

Slides

Slide 1.1 shows the arrangement of a powder camera.

Slide 1.3 gives an X-ray powder picture taken with sodium chloride, similar to the one taken in the film. The reflection at a Bragg angle θ of 15.9° (line 2) can be identified on this slide, and students can check that the angle is the same as that found in the second film but using a single crystal and a Geiger counter. See figure 19 a.

Evidence for the polycrystalline nature of metals

If granulated zinc is melted in a crucible and allowed to cool it will form crystals which are visible to the naked eye if the piece of zinc is broken in half. There may be some advantage in using a magnifying glass to inspect the broken surfaces. The ends of the piece of cast bismuth from the O-level crystals kit (item 3F) are very similar in appearance to the broken surfaces of the zinc.

The large crystal areas on galvanized steel may be shown, or recalled. Photographs of the microscopic crystals in metals are to be found in the following:
Nuffield O-level Chemistry, *The structure of substances*.
Moffatt, Pearsall, Wulff, *The structure and properties of materials*.
Scientific American book *Materials*.

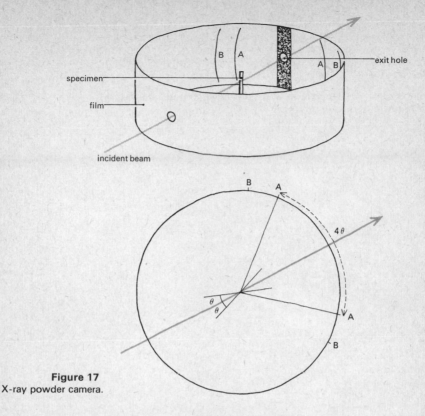

Figure 17
X-ray powder camera.

Film loops of X-ray powder photography

Turning back to X-rays, the third film in the series shows powdered sodium chloride exposed to X-rays. The resulting jumble of tiny crystals will have a few facing in the right direction to reflect at all possible angles, and a strip of film wrapped round the specimen can catch and record the diffracted radiation.

Why are the 'lines' on the film curved? X-rays coming from the specimen at any one angle to the incoming beam will lie on the surface of a cone, which cuts the film in a curved line.

The film also shows the result of replacing the powdered crystal by a copper wire. The result is a very similar-looking pattern. Students should have objected by now that copper does not look crystalline, as large salt crystals do, having no regular shape. Why should one suppose that copper atoms are arranged in regular patterns?

Students' book

The X-ray powder photographs, figures 19 *a* and *b*, appear in question 20. Question 20 *a* uses the sodium chloride photograph to practise measuring angles. Question 20 *b* obtains the size of a copper atom by the argument opposite. The questions could be done at home, saving teaching time for discussion. Question 21 is more general, suited to class discussion.

Many teachers will prefer to develop a class discussion around the slides, rather than to send students away to work on their own.

The existence of sharp X-ray diffraction lines is the evidence which decides the point. The similarity between the patterns for powdered salt and copper suggests that the copper crystals exist but are too small to see easily.

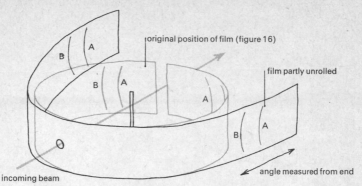

Figure 18
Powder camera film partly unrolled.

Analysing the powder photographs: the size of a copper atom

Figure 18 shows the film from figure 17, cut across the place where the X-rays left the camera, and partly unrolled. Figure 19 *a* shows the unrolled film taken with sodium chloride (slide 1.3). The line marked 2, now near the end of the photograph, lies at a Bragg angle of 15.9°, the same angle as was found in the film loop using a single crystal of sodium chloride and a Geiger counter; the X-ray wavelengths were the same.

Figure 19 *b* shows the result for a copper wire. Lines 1, 2, and 3 will be found to lie at angles to the original beam direction of nearly 44°, 50°, and 74°; two close together and another further round. The Bragg angles are half these values.

The wavelength of the 3 cm radiation used in demonstration 1.4 depends on a number of factors and will not always be the same. But for a typical value $(3.15 \times 10^{-2}$ m), the three angles measured in the earlier experiment with the 50 mm diameter balls are almost the same as those in the X-ray photograph, where the wavelength was 0.154 nm. If they are nearly the same, some student may suggest that copper atoms are packed in the same way as the ball model and that the ratio of their diameters is equal to the ratio of the wavelengths. The atom's diameter comes to 2.5×10^{-10} m. Others may be more cautious, for there have been few stages in the argument with inescapable conclusions. But it may be pointed out that X-ray analysis of a substance has often been started by thinking of a structure which would give the scattering observed from that substance, and then supposing that the substance has that structure. More sophisticated methods are now used, and the observations are more accurate and more complete than in the case we have discussed, but the logic is not much more direct.

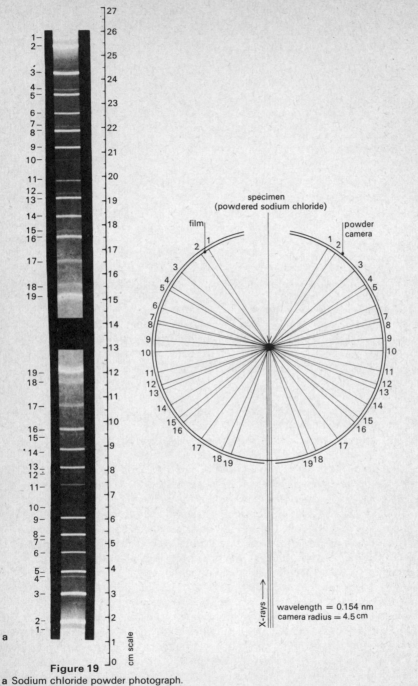

Figure 19
a Sodium chloride powder photograph.
b Copper powder photograph.

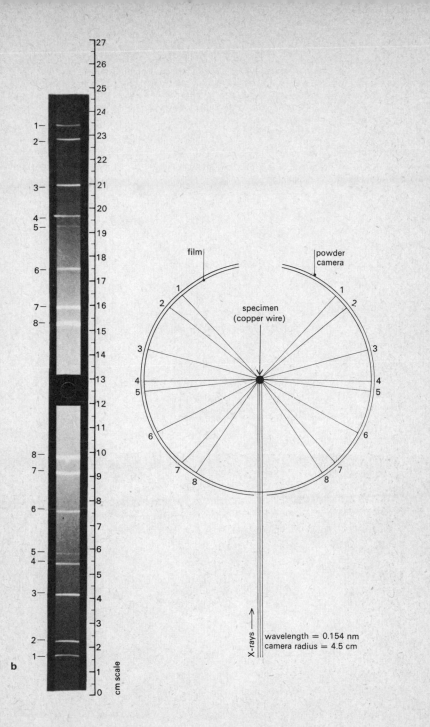

b

cm scale

film

powder camera

specimen
(copper wire)

1
2
3
4
5
6
7
8

1
2
3
4
5
6
7
8

X-rays ⟶

wavelength = 0.154 nm
camera radius = 4.5 cm

Nuffield Advanced Chemistry

Topic 1 deals with the mole as the standard amount of substance. *Topic 3,* which might come close in time to the work of this Unit, mentions several ways of estimating the Avogadro constant (*a*) in an oil film experiment, (*b*) from the Faraday and the charge on an electron, (*c*) from radioactive decay. The idea of determining structures with X-rays and finding the constant that way comes later, in *Topic 8*. The treatment in *Topic 8* is complementary to that suggested in this Unit, emphasizing optical analogues rather than Bragg's Law.

Students' book

Questions 15 and 16 take students through the argument for the value of the Avogadro constant. They might replace classroom teaching.

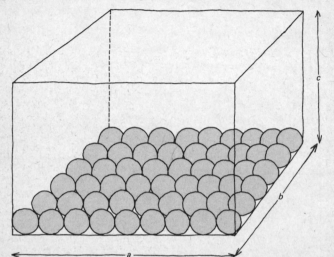

a

b

The Avogadro constant

Knowing the size of a copper atom, and the arrangement of the atoms, it is possible to find the Avogadro constant: that is, the number of copper atoms in a lump of copper of mass 63.6 g. Indeed, such calculations are at present the most accurate method available for finding the Avogadro constant.

What is the volume of a mole of copper atoms? The density 8930 kg m^{-3} is needed, giving a volume of 7.13×10^{-6} m³.

To work out how many copper atoms of diameter D will fit into that volume, think about making a greengrocer's stack of atoms (figure 6, demonstration 1.3) to build a rectangular brick of copper of sides a, b, c.

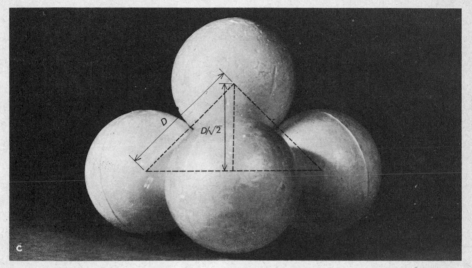

Figure 20
a One layer of atoms in a box.
b Four atoms in lower layer.
c Atom in next layer is $D/\sqrt{2}$ above lower layer.

A number of atoms a/D will fit into the length a, and a number b/D into the width b, so that a number ab/D^2 completes the layer of atoms in square array with which the stack starts (figure 20 a).

Further layers are made of atoms nesting between four others in the layer below (figure 20 b and c). The four supporting atoms form a square of side D, diagonal $D\sqrt{2}$, and an atom in the layer above spans this diagonal. Its centre lies a distance $D/\sqrt{2}$ above the centres of those below it. If the geometry seems hard, the factor $\sqrt{2}$ can be taken from measurements made with the polystyrene spheres.

Scaling the analogue experiment

Both copper and the crystal model have the same structure: face-centred cubic.

For reflections from, say, the hexagonally arranged layers of each:

X-rays and copper $\lambda_{\text{X-rays}} = 2d_{\text{copper}} \sin \theta$

microwaves and the model $\lambda_{\text{microwaves}} = 2d_{\text{model}} \sin \theta$

The angles θ will be the same if $\dfrac{d_{\text{copper}}}{d_{\text{model}}} = \dfrac{\lambda_{\text{X-rays}}}{\lambda_{\text{microwaves}}}$

Because the structures are the same, the ball and atom diameters D are in the same ratio as the spacing d of corresponding kinds of layers.

$$\frac{D_{\text{atom}}}{D_{\text{ball}}} = \frac{d_{\text{copper}}}{d_{\text{model}}}$$

The diameter found in this way is the diameter an atom would have if it were a hard ball touching its neighbours.

Theory leading to Bragg's Law $\lambda = 2d \sin \theta$

Students who have had enough could now pass to page 47, omitting Bragg's Law. This Law will be needed in the second year, for electron diffraction in Unit 10, *Waves, particles, and atoms,* and is part of the complete course.

It could be postponed, either to the end of the course or to Unit 4, *Waves and oscillations.*

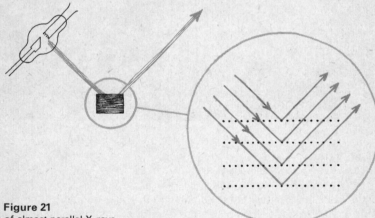

Figure 21
Scattering of almost parallel X-rays.

The numbers of layers that can be fitted into the height c is thus $c\sqrt{2}/D$, and the number of atoms that make up the brick of volume abc is $abc\sqrt{2}/D^3$.

If the volume $abc = 7.13 \times 10^{-6}$ m³ mol⁻¹, the volume of a mole of copper atoms, then the number of atoms in one mole is:

$$\frac{7.13 \times 10^{-6}\sqrt{2}}{(2.5 \times 10^{-10})^3} = 6.4 \times 10^{23} \text{ mol}^{-1}.$$

This is fairly close to the accepted value of the Avogadro constant. A small error in the diameter of the atom makes a big difference. A diameter 2.55×10^{-10} m would give nearly the accepted value of the Avogadro constant.

Simple argument for scaling down the analogue experiment

Is the diffraction of X-rays by copper the same as that of microwaves by the crystal model, only smaller? Figure 15 (page 33) showed what might be happening.

Suppose figure 15 were on half the scale. The layer spacing would be half as much; so would any path difference between layers. If the wavelength were half as much, any path difference that was before equal to λ, or $\lambda/2$, would still have that value, as long as the angle stays the same (to keep angled path differences on the same scale). So it seems fair to scale down the analogue experiment in the ratio of the wavelengths.

The fourth film loop on X-ray diffraction shows how the X-ray wavelength could have been measured. It shows X-rays diffracted at nearly grazing incidence by a plane-ruled grating. The wavelength is 0.154 nm.

Diffraction of X-rays

On the scale of individual layers of atoms, the X-ray source is enormously far away, and so is the film. So a simple theory treats the problem as one of parallel beams reaching the layers of atoms (figure 21).

Students' book

Question 22 gives the argument for the Bragg equation $\lambda = 2d \sin \theta$ and asks for critical thinking about it. See the alternative offered in Nuffield O-level Physics *Teachers' guide V*, page 328.

Textbooks

These can also be used, now or later for revision. See:

Arons, *Development of concepts of physics,* page 826 (probably the best).

Baez, *The new college physics,* page 597.

Bennet, *Electricity and modern physics,* page 274.

Caro, McDonell, and Spicer, *Modern physics,* page 38.

PSSC *Physics* (2nd edition) page 631 develops the Law, but for neutrons diffracted from a crystal, which might interest a very bright student.

Rogers, *Physics for the inquiring mind,* page 186.

References to these books appear in the answer to question 22.

Simplifying the Bragg theory

Figure 22 is deliberately drawn with fuzzy layers, to distract the student from the fact that a layer is a regular array of atoms. The theory offered is really a theory of demonstration 1.6, with tiles, rather than of demonstration 1.4, with a regular structure of spheres, in which the scattering centres in a layer are separated from each other by distances of the order of a wavelength.

A Bragg plane within a crystal, or a layer of regularly arranged spheres such as those from which the crystal model was built will, on its own, act like a two-dimensional diffraction grating. There will certainly be a zero order reflection obeying the usual law of reflection, but from one layer there can be other directions in which there is an appreciable intensity, as with any diffraction grating in reflection. However, when there are many layers, the only direction in which all layers contribute amplitudes in step is the zero order direction obeying the usual law of reflection.

Whilst an occasional first-rate student might be encouraged to think about these difficulties, most are not likely to expect a difference between a layer of spheres and a flat tile, or to appreciate arguments that their similarity might be in doubt, as was suggested on page 31.

Film loops

The Longman Loop 'The diffraction of X-rays by a crystal' and Ealing Scientific 'Bragg reflection of waves' both show ripple tank analogues of Bragg reflection.

Either loop could be useful, though neither is essential. Demonstration of Bragg reflection in a ripple tank is not easy, but can be achieved especially if Schlieren techniques are employed. Arranging such a demonstration would be a task for a particularly skilled student who felt his or her abilities under-employed at this stage.

Bragg's Law

Demonstration 1.6 shows that one flat tile reflects some radiation at all angles obeying the law of reflection. A stack of tiles reflects it at just one particular angle, still obeying the usual reflection law. Demonstration 1.4 was similar, but the model crystal seemed to have several sets of layers capable of producing a strong reflection as in 1.6.

Figure 22 shows parallel radiation falling on a set of layers at a glancing angle θ, reflected by each layer at this same angle. The radiation going via B travels an extra distance X B Y, or $2d \sin \theta$, and that going via C the same extra distance over that via B. If $\lambda = 2d \sin \theta$, the radiation from successive layers will be in step, and a strong beam will emerge.

Suppose $0.9\ \lambda = 2d \sin \theta$. The radiation from the sixth layer will be 4.5 wavelengths behind that from the first, giving zero resultant from these two. That from the nth surface will destroy that from the $(n-5)^{\text{th}}$ surface throughout the structure. If the radiation penetrates many layers, the reflected beam will be weak except in one very particular direction, for which $\lambda = 2d \sin \theta$.

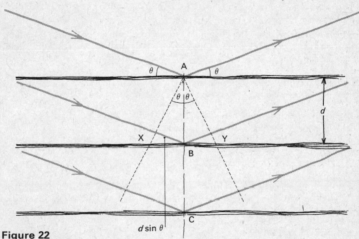

Figure 22
Bragg theory of diffraction.

The Avogadro constant and the wavelength of X-rays

Teachers may wish to note privately that the Avogadro constant calculation from the size of an atom as determined by X-rays depends in the end on being able to measure the wavelength of the X-rays with a grating. It is a difficult technique, but it has been done accurately, and so this method offers at present the best determination of the Avogadro constant. Such is the curious interconnectedness of physics, that counting atoms depends on making and using good diffraction gratings.

Instructions for making the sodium chloride model

See Appendix B for instructions for building the model shown in figure 25.

Reading

The *Scientific American* offprint 'X-ray crystallography', by Sir Lawrence Bragg, is quite remarkably apt at this point. It mentions the structure and X-ray diffraction of NaCl, and describes recent work in molecular biology.

Optional further work with sodium chloride

Teachers may like to consider salt further. The X-ray photograph, slide 1.3 (*Students' book,* figure 9) has a strong line at a Bragg angle of 15° 15'. The spacing *d* for this line comes to 2.8×10^{-10} m, which happens to be the spacing between nearest sodium and chlorine ions.

Cleaving

Students can cleave salt crystals. The cleaving is best done with a sharp chisel, holding the crystal in the angle of an L-shaped anvil. Suitable crystals can be bought from suppliers. The chisel or anvil may rust if not cleaned after contact with salt.

The planes along which the crystal cleaves are related to the structure. The ions come apart along planes which contain positive and negative ions in close contact (see figure 23).

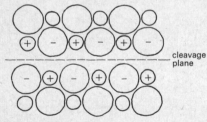
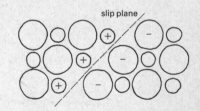

Figures 23 and 24
Cleavage plane of NaCl and slip plane of NaCl.

Slip

It is possible, but harder, to show that sodium chloride crystals will slip along certain planes. The slip planes contain layers of ions of one kind facing ions of the other kind (figure 24), and it is reasonable that a positive ion can slide round from the hollow between negative ions to the next-door hollow. Compare the cleavage plane: to slip on this plane, each ion would have to move against the strong repulsion of an ion of the same sign.

X-ray analysis of structures – an overall view

The use of X-rays to investigate the arrangement of atoms and molecules in substances is nowadays widespread, as they are used by metallurgists, chemists, biologists, and many others besides physicists. The information from X-ray diffraction is used to make models or draw maps showing where the atoms are in a structure or a molecule, and such models or maps may help to answer questions about the behaviour of the materials concerned.

The story began with substances like salt, chosen by Sir Lawrence Bragg and his father because they thought it would be easy to analyse. A model, figure 25, of the structure of sodium chloride can be shown with the explanation that structures such as these can be worked out by methods similar to, but more detailed than our sketchy treatment of copper.

The large Cl^- ions and the small Na^+ ions can be indicated with the remark that later in the course (Unit 3) the forces that hold ions together like this will be studied.

Figure 25
Model of sodium chloride crystal.

To show slip planes, a small cleaved specimen about $10 \times 4 \times 2$ mm is squeezed longways in a suitable Bunsen clip or in a small vice (figure 26).

Slip lines can be seen if the crystal is deformed between crossed polaroids, under the microscope. Note that the crystals are hygroscopic, and should be handled with tweezers and stored in a desiccator.

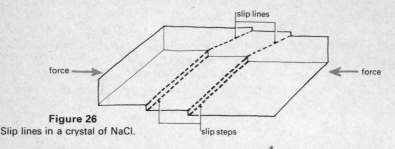

Figure 26
Slip lines in a crystal of NaCl.

The work of the crystallographer

This brief 'lantern lecture' aims to give students a sense of the wide possibilities of work in this area. It would be good if it aroused interest in the significant way in which the discovery of X-ray analysis has changed physics and other subjects. Solids are now the subject of extensive study, whilst they were almost a closed book fifty years ago. The most momentous consequences may yet be in the future, for a knowledge of the structure of the chemicals which rule life itself will surely be a potent force for good or evil.

The slides offered make one possible story: teachers can bring it up to date and add other material in which they have a special interest.

Slides

1.10	a metal alloy — X-ray diffraction
1.11	haemoglobin — X-ray diffraction
1.12	structure of $TlAlF_4$
1.13	structure of p-diphenylbenzene
1.6	polythene (undrawn) — X-ray diffraction
1.7	polythene (drawn) — X-ray diffraction
1.15	lysozyme molecule

For fuller details, see list of slides, page 101.

The work of the crystallographer

The argument about copper has given a glimpse of the work of the crystallographer. His task is to record and study diffraction patterns and to try to argue from them to the atomic arrangements which caused them. Some diffraction patterns tell something of the inner regularity of structures even to the untrained eye (slide 1.10), others show little or nothing except to the expert (slide 1.11). Each of these photographs shows large numbers of diffraction spots (maxima), each associated with some sets of planes satisfying Bragg's Law, and each photograph shows only a small fraction of the spots which the complex crystals involved can produce. The task of interpretation is usually difficult and often impossible, but the need to know the atomic arrangements in metals, minerals, organic and inorganic crystals, liquids, glasses, fibres, and the highly complex molecules of living material has been a constant spur to extensive studies of diffraction methods.

Because they study the structures of all types of materials, crystallographers can be found in the laboratories of physics, chemistry, geology, mineralogy, metallurgy, fibre technology, biochemistry, or molecular biology. One might produce results like an intricate array of tellurium, aluminium, and fluorine atoms (slide 1.12), another will be interested in the atomic architecture of molecules which can be studied when they pack together in crystals like p-diphenylbenzene (slide 1.13), and yet another will study the irregular arrangements of atoms in liquids, glasses, or plastics (slides 1.6, 1.7) where sharp spots or lines give way to fuzzy haloes.

The crowning achievement of this type of research has been the determination of the structures of protein molecules. Each of these contains so many atoms that it is very difficult to show a picture of the result at all! Slide 1.15 shows some of the tangled molecular chain in the biologically important chemical lysozyme. Several thousand diffraction spots were measured to obtain this result. X-ray studies have helped to settle the structures of haemoglobin, of proteins, and of DNA and RNA, the messengers of heredity.

Talking about models

One aim of the course is for students to be able to argue about what it is to do physics. Models are so widely used that we suggest an early, if light, introduction of this theme. It is not our aim to make students learn, for later repetition, some one or other particular view. Our aim is that they should discuss what doing science is like, and we suggest that teachers indicate that there is room for debate. For this reason, most of the material opposite is in the form of questions. Larger questions may arise. A model clearly does not pretend to be certain, complete knowledge. Do scientists know anything certainly and completely? Perhaps a student will think that mathematicians, at least, know for sure. 'Two plus two is always four.' A view they may not have met suggests that this is not a fact at all, but a rule for making marks on paper in the game of arithmetic. Like the rule for moving knights in chess, it could be followed or broken, but is not the kind of thing which is true or false. Some students welcome a little philosophy, others have learned — wrongly we think — to despise it. But it should be made clear to them that there are here no certainties, only debates which some think deep and interesting and others think remote and useless.

Students' book

See questions 14 and 23. Both are better suited to discussion than individual work.

Other references

See Dirac, 'The evolution of the physicist's picture of nature.' Here Dirac suggests that the best way to get a true equation is to look for a beautiful equation, never minding the facts. See Watson, *The double helix,* for a description of the conceiving of a model (of DNA), with only minimal access to experimental facts.
Bronowski, *The common sense of science*, and Bondi, *The Universe at large*, also offer ideas about the use of models in scientific inquiry.
See also *Nuffield O-level Physics, Teachers' guide V,* pages 81–3, and *Teachers' guide III,* page 281. Chapter 24 of Rogers, *Physics for the inquiring mind,* is good value.

Thinking about scientific inquiry

We quote the following passage by Karl Popper. It appears in the *Students' book* as well.

> 'The way in which knowledge progresses, and especially our scientific knowledge, is by unjustified (and unjustifiable) anticipations, by guesses, by tentative solutions to our problems, by conjectures. These conjectures are controlled by criticism; that is, by attempted refutations, which include severely critical tests. They may survive these tests; but they can never be positively justified: they can neither be established as certainly true nor even as "probable" (in the sense of the probability calculus). Criticism of our conjectures is of decisive importance: by bringing out our mistakes it makes us understand the difficulties of the problem which we are trying to solve. This is how we become better acquainted with our problem, and able to propose more mature solutions: the very refutation of a theory — that is, of any serious tentative solution to our problem — is always a step forward that takes us nearer to the truth. And this is how we can learn from our mistakes.
>
> 'As we learn from our mistakes our knowledge grows, even though we may never know — that is, know for certain. Since our knowledge can grow, there can be no reason here for despair of reason. And since we can never know for certain, there can be no authority here for any claim to authority, for conceit over our knowledge, or for smugness.'
>
> *From the preface by the author, K. R. Popper, to* Conjectures and refutations *(1963), Routledge & Kegan Paul.*

Preparation for students' reports at the end of Part Three

Here, we shall suggest asking some students to collect and report information on such materials as concrete, fibreglass, plywood, and toughened glass. They may also want to obtain or make samples. If the teacher chooses to do this, the work will need to be assigned at about this point.

Models

Assemblies of glued-up polystyrene balls have been offered as, in some way, 'good' models of copper or salt. Obviously, copper atoms are not made of polystyrene. What features of copper does the model represent well? What features does it not represent? Some further questions may help:

Are copper atoms hard, rather fragile spheres?

Need copper atoms be spherical for the model to serve?

If copper atoms were stacked in a different pattern, would it still serve?

What about the electrons which conduct electricity in copper; are they represented?

The model has no missing spheres, but is it not likely that some atoms out of 10^{23} or so in a lump of copper would be missing or misplaced?

For use in the microwave experiment, metal balls would be bad, as the microwaves would not reach inside the structure appreciably. (Only the outer layers would reflect radiation like a mirror, or more precisely, like a grating.) But copper atoms are metal, or aren't they?

Sometimes models are used to help one to visualize or remember what things are like; sometimes as tools for working out what will happen. Probably the models discussed so far have been used mainly in the first way, although knowledge of how atoms are arranged may make it possible to predict or explain the behaviour of a material. Examples of this process follow in the rest of this Unit.

A model for predicting may have been met at O-level; the Greek scheme of spheres carrying planets and stars was a device for predicting how the stars would move next, not a model of how the heavens were supposed really to be. Often, in physics, the second sort of model takes the form of an equation — a mathematical model. The equation $s = \frac{1}{2} at^2$ is a device for predicting the distance moved by accelerating bodies. Like other models, it has limits — there must be no air resistance — but within its limits it is a good predicting device. The course will include other mathematical models.

In developing the model of copper, it was not possible to look inside copper and build up the balls in the same pattern as the atoms. The model was guessed, and then tested. Are there other examples where physicists thought of an idea first and looked at the facts later?

'Theories are nets: only he who casts will catch.'
(*Novalis*.)

Is it proper to guess in science? Can it be shown that a guess is true, or probable, or false? Such questions may well arise and should be encouraged.

Part Three

Stretching and breaking

Time: up to two weeks.

Purpose and suggested sequence of Part Three

The suggested sequence begins with empirical experience, leading to some fairly accurate measurement. Some terms of value appear: 'elastic', 'plastic', 'brittle', 'stress', 'strain', and a few others. Some simple experimental design is called for.

Then the stretching and breaking of materials are discussed from an atomic point of view, linking the work with Part Two. The stiffness of an atomic bond is estimated, and will be used later (Unit 4). The breaking of copper and glass is contrasted, with the influence of cracks and (less fully) dislocations emerging from the contrast.

Finally, what the engineer can do to moderate the influence of cracks is looked at, considering composite materials including reinforced concrete and fibreglass. It is suggested that this discussion be based largely on students' reading and brief talks from them about what they have read.

Students' book

This is a suitable time to return to questions 1 to 7. See also question 26.

Experiment
1.7   Feeling materials stretch and break

Available to each group:

2B	copper wire, 32 s.w.g. bare, 1 m lengths
1054	stainless steel wire, 44 s.w.g., 1 m lengths (item 7A may serve)
1053	PVC insulating tape or similar thick sticky tape
23	microscope
1053	rubber bands, 50–100 mm long, assorted thicknesses
529	scissors
1054	0.2 m length of 3 mm diameter soda glass rod
503–6	retort stand base, rod, boss, and clamp
508	Bunsen burner
32	weight, 1 kg
1053	thin string
35	S-hooks
530	pliers
44/2	G-clamp, small

Accessible if possible:

1055	micrometer screw gauge
	or
1055	Vernier callipers
81	spring balance 10 N
40	pulley on clamp, single
31/2	weight hangers with slotted weights (0.1 kg)

Part Two concerned the arrangement of atoms in materials. Such information is of practical importance, for it may help students to understand why materials behave as they do, and suggest ways of making better, more useful materials. Part Three is about how materials stretch and break, why they do not all stretch and break in the same way, and what the engineer can do to improve their performance.

Introduction to experiments on stretching and breaking

One can ask what a bridge engineer needs to know about a new steel he is thinking of using. Will a long bridge bend more under the load of a heavy lorry than a short bridge whose other dimensions are similar? What does the designer have to consider when choosing steel girders? Is steel the best material? Is the stretching of copper or aluminium of interest to the designer of high voltage transmission lines? Such questions serve to introduce the following experiments, about how much materials stretch, when they break, and in what way they break or yield.

Experiment
1.7 Feeling materials stretch and break

Students may be invited to pull samples of materials in their hands, with the purpose of seeing what happens and of designing ways of measuring what happens. It may be well to forecast the small extensions to be expected, and ask for ways of making the extensions bigger, so that the importance of length may emerge naturally.

The importance of cross-section may be introduced by supplying rubber bands of various thicknesses and asking whether the rubber in all of them is equally stretchy.

Brief written notes about what they observe and the rough sizes of forces and extensions found are worth having, for the next experiments will involve each group in designing a reasonably accurate way of measuring the stretchiness and strength of one material and they will need to know enough about it to design a sensible experiment.

The materials suggested are:

glass

copper

steel (warn students of the dangers from a broken wire whipping through the air)

rubber

(polythene – optional extra).

Optional:

    1053   polythene sheet

    1053   razor blade and straight edge

Organization

It is suggested that each group of students should handle each piece of material in this experiment, taking no more than one double period to handle all of them.

The number of sets of apparatus to be available will depend on whether students move round from station to station or are all provided with each material.

Fixing wires

Students can, in experiment 1.7, pull the wires between their hands if the ends are wrapped round suitable dowels. It may be better to show them a way of fixing the ends of the wires which can also be used in experiment 1.8.

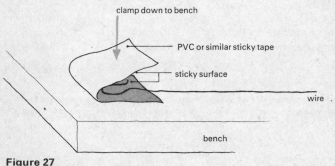

Figure 27
Securing the end of a wire.

Figure 27 shows a simple and effective method for fixing one end. The wire end, with a loop in it, is sandwiched between the sticky faces of a piece of thick strong adhesive tape and the sandwich is clamped to the bench. The G-clamp should press on the wire loop through the tape, but not on the bare wire. This method is effective for the thin wires and small loads suggested, and the wire rarely breaks at the fixing point, whilst being held there very rigidly.

Figure 28
Wire attached to S-hook.

The end of the wire to be pulled can be attached to an S-hook by winding at least five turns tightly round the hook and securing the free end (figure 28). In experiment 1.8, weights or spring balances can be attached to the hook.

Microscopes should be available for inspecting the fractures, so that the question of how the materials break can be answered.

The question, 'Is steel really the strongest of these materials?' could, in discussion, bring out the need to calculate stresses rather than simple stretching forces.

To save time, now and later, the class can be shown how to pull a straight glass thread as well as how to fix and load it, and how to fix the ends of a wire for pulling.

Pulling a straight glass thread

Hold the top of a glass rod in a stand and clamp it so that it is about one metre above the bench or floor, and is vertical. Tie a one kilogramme weight to the lower end with string. A clove-hitch is suitable. Support the weight with one hand and heat the middle of the glass rod over as short a length as possible until it is red hot. The lower part of the rod may need to be supported. Remove the flame and release the weight; this will then pull out a straight glass thread which has glass rod at each end so that it can be pulled in the hands.

Safety

Glass and steel are potentially dangerous materials to break, and warnings will be needed. A bin for broken glass is essential.

The steel wire is very thin, so that not much energy is stored in it when it fractures, and danger from a broken end whipping back is minimized. If thicker wire is used, it could be sleeved with rubber tubing or be stretched in a simple tunnel made from three lengths of timber built into a **U** shape. The broken end of a steel wire is sharp, and students should be warned of the danger of cuts.

Optional – stretching polythene

Strips of polythene about 0.2 m by 10 mm, cut with clean, not ragged, edges pull out in an interesting way (see figure 29).

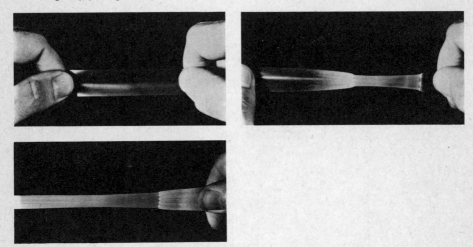

Figure 29
Pulling a strip of polythene.

The strip necks at one place until it is about half as wide as before, and the sides of the neck pull along until all the strip has narrowed down. The narrow part is usually striated longways, and will easily split in that direction. The force needed to pull the neck open is roughly constant, but when all the strip has narrowed, the material is fairly elastic and has a higher modulus than before.

If the narrowed strip is boiled in water, it returns more or less to its original length, though the striations remain.

Summary of observations

Glass softens gradually as it is heated. (By comparison, heated solder melts suddenly.) Glass pulls into long thin threads. The thread does not stretch appreciably, but will carry a surprisingly big load. The strength is unreliable, and an old, much handled thread may break sooner than a fresh one. Glass 'snaps' or fractures cleanly with no evidence of soft yielding (the broken ends fit together).

Comparison of students' estimates of breaking loads will bring out the need to take the cross-section of the fibre into account.

Copper yields and is permanently stretched by a surprising amount before it breaks. Both the stretched and unstretched wire show a small amount of springy stretching, after which each will recover its previous length. Students often miss this; those who spot it are becoming good observers. The word 'elastic' can be introduced.

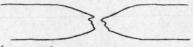

Figure 30
Necking at point of fracture of copper wire.

The broken ends of the wire are necked, as in figure 30, evidence of plastic (soft, slipping) yielding. Under the microscope, the wire near the fracture may have a rough appearance.

Steel wire shows elastic stretching, but breaks after it has been stretched by a small amount. There is evidence of soft yielding in the neck formed at the point of fracture. The elasticity and recovery to the unstretched shape is revealed also by its annoying springiness and tendency to lash back.

Rubber stretches by an astonishing amount, and will recover its original length. It pulls easily at first, but at large extensions large extra forces stretch it very little more; this is a good place to introduce the doubt whether the ratio of force to extension will be a constant quantity for other materials, and the need to test the point. Rubber becomes thinner when stretched: is the volume constant? (It is, nearly.) It shows some creep if left loaded, and its stretchiness changes with temperature.

The class could be asked to speculate about how rubber molecules could allow this unusual behaviour. They may think of long molecules coiling and uncoiling. More about the nature of rubber follows later.

Terms to be heard and terms to be remembered

In the discussion of experiment 1.7, students can be asked to try to say clearly what they saw. The terms 'elastic', 'plastic' (ductile), 'brittle', can be introduced as useful shorthand. Students should be expected, as time goes by, to understand and be able to use these terms adequately. They will be asked to use them as tools of scientific communication, not to reproduce definitions from memory.

The terms 'stress' and 'strain' will be needed, with their quantitative meanings. Students will be expected to remember the way in which a Young modulus is calculated.

Other terms are useful, but their use need not be insisted upon. 'Stiffness' is a good word for an elastic modulus, distinguishing it from 'strength', which describes the stress needed to fracture a material.

'Tough' is a good way of saying 'not brittle' or 'not susceptible to cracking'. A table may help:

	Tough	Stiff	Strong
Biscuits	no	yes	no
Steel	yes	yes	yes
Nylon	yes	no	fairly
Jelly	no (it cracks)	no	no

Add 'light', and most worthwhile information about the material is represented.

Students' book

Questions 4, 5, 7 concern the use of terms to describe materials. Questions 24 and 25 are about stress and strain.

Books

Gordon, *The new science of strong materials,* Chapter 2, discusses terms informally. The article by Kelly, 'The nature of composite materials', in the *Scientific American* book, *Materials,* illustrates the use of the terms. A student may be reading this now, in preparation for a report at the end of this Unit.

Time effects, temperature effects

It may amuse teachers to have one or two light-hearted demonstrations at hand. They show that there are further complications to the study of deformation.

Suggested equipment:

1053	silicone putty
4A	drinking straw
1053	potato
1053	rubber band
1021	aerosol freezer
1053	needle
1055	hammer

Stress, strain, the Young modulus, breaking strength

Loads and extensions will serve to compare wires, but to compare materials or work out the strength of a wire of untried thickness requires the ideas of stress and strain.

The dependence of extension on length should have emerged, and may seem natural if a long wire is thought of as two short ones end to end, both stretching equally. The meaning of the term *strain* can now be given.

The dependence on cross-sectional area can be approached by thinking of a thick wire as two thinner ones side by side, each needing its own pull. *Stress* can be introduced. Trials with rubber bands of differing thickness may be enough to convince the class that these new notions are sensible. If, however, the ideas seem hard, groups of students can try pulling long and short wires, or rubber cords, of the same thickness, and thick and thin wires or cords of the same length, to test whether extension divided by original length and force divided by cross-sectional area are constant quantities.

The breaking strength of a material — the stress at which it fails — seems worth measuring with some accuracy. So does the stress needed to stretch it to some standard strain, for this will record how little the material will give under load in some applications. 'Stiffness' is a word that usefully expresses the property, for many loads in practice tend to bend a material (bridges, aircraft wings, or a sewing machine needle under the pull of the cotton), stretching it on the outside of the bend and squashing it on the inside.

Bending and stretching are linked; the quantity to be measured in the next group of experiments is the ratio of changes of stretching stress to stretching strain, if it is acceptably constant. It is called the Young modulus.

It is convenient now to suggest that results of the stretching experiments to come be presented as stress–strain graphs, and to agree on units. The connection of the slope of the graph with the modulus can be brought out, particularly if students guess, from previous experience, the form of the graph for, say, rubber.

Physicists and engineers are fond of quantities like an elastic modulus, for when such quantities exist they are capable of containing much information very compactly. Books of data are full of such quantities.

Time

a Silicone putty (potty putty) flows like a viscous liquid if left alone, and can be moulded into a ball. If the ball is thrown against a wall, it bounces, behaving elastically at high stress rates. If hit with a hammer, it fractures.

b A drinking straw makes a poor dagger. It can however be driven clean through a raw potato with a rapid enough stabbing action. It should be thrust very rapidly at the potato with a 'karate' chopping action. The straw can be held firmly in a clenched fist and a determined attempt should be made to get the swing to follow through to the other side of the potato. A swing which is aimed at just hitting the surface will fail. The potato should be held between finger and thumb so that the top and bottom are clear.

Temperature

Freeze the middle part of a 10 mm wide rubber strip using an aerosol freezer. When the strip is pulled, the cold portion does not stretch nearly as much as the ends.

Figure 31
Stretching rubber cooled in the middle.

Heat treatment of steel

Bend a sewing needle with pliers until it snaps. Some elastic bending occurs. Heat another needle gently until it is discoloured, and cool it slowly, when it can be bent easily. If the same needle is heated red hot and quenched in water, it will now snap if bent between the fingers.

Experiments
1.8 Measurements of the Young modulus and breaking strength

Apparatus as for experiment 1.7 with the addition of:

501	metre rules
1053	Sellotape

Access to:

1055	micrometer screw gauge
81	spring balance, 10 N and higher ranges (50 N, or 5 kgf is the upper limit)
31/2	weight hanger with slotted weights (0.1 kg)
40	pulley on clamp, single
533	plastic bucket (if weights are in short supply)

Possible needs:

materials for making levers, etc. to magnify extensions

Vernier device for measuring extensions

conventional Young modulus apparatus

weights, several kilogrammes (for rubber)

Group of experiments

1.8 **Measurements of the Young modulus and breaking strength**

Each group of students can have one material and be asked to devise a reasonably accurate, simple (and safe) experiment to obtain a stress–strain graph, a value or range of values of the Young modulus, and the breaking stress.

For glass, it is best to ask only for the breaking stress, unless there is an especially skilled student who could devise a way of measuring the very small extensions (less than 0.1 per cent).

Polythene can be added as an optional extra, if a wider range of materials is wanted.

It is worth spending time discussing the meaning of students' graphs, especially where they curve.

Scientists, engineers, economists, and businessmen find that information can be represented graphically for many purposes. The art of reading information from a graph is one well worth acquiring.

The microscopes are not needed. Copper and steel wire should be available in any reasonable lengths asked for.

It is suggested that each group of students work with one material only. In all but small classes, comparison results for most materials will be available, so that there is a basis for critical discussion.

The problem presented to the student is one of experimental design. Later on in the course, the class will often have to accept the apparatus provided, but at this stage it would be good for them to design their own. The results will be poorer than they would be with, say, Searle's apparatus, but important lessons about experimenting may emerge, particularly from failures of design.

A scale marked in millimetres will serve if the metal wires are at least 2 m long, preferably longer. A Sellotape flag on the wires can be used as an indicator, though some may prefer Verniers if they are available, while others may devise levers to magnify the extensions.

The problems with rubber are simpler, and ink marks on a rubber band cut to form a single thread will do very well.

It is convenient to encourage students to stretch copper and steel wires horizontally, both for ease of measurement and to allow long lengths to be used.

Rubber can be stretched horizontally or vertically, and the glass thread is best broken by hanging weights on a string tied with a clove-hitch to the glass rod from which it was pulled. A bucket slowly filled with water makes a convenient large weight, but it must be suspended close to the floor!

Measurement of the elastic modulus of glass should be reserved for the rare enthusiast.

A group of experiments shared among the class

This is the first occasion on which it is suggested that pairs of students can be sent off with different tasks relating to a common theme, requiring them to report findings to the class afterwards. This policy for the Advanced course is one to be developed early, and will have to be explained to the class. The ability to learn from the work of others, to present one's own work intelligibly, and to meet questions and criticism are, we hope, going to be developed by such a method of work. It should be especially relevant since students will be learning more and more from secondhand evidence in the future. It is hoped that the interest and responsibility of doing something unique, and the feedback inherent in having to explain it to others, will help to raise the quality of work done.

Copying facilities would be a great help. Students could draw graphs or results straight onto the master of a spirit duplicator (or photocopier) for general circulation. Reports need to be discussed, and perhaps some poor ones re-written. Trials suggest that the quality of reports, disappointing at first, has improved a good deal by the second or third occasion.

This sharing and reporting will take time. We think it will be time well spent.

Students' book

See questions 26 to 30. Question 26 is about deformations observed on a photograph. Question 27 is about law-like behaviour, taking Hooke's Law as an example. Questions 28 to 30 use the idea of the Young modulus in numerical problems.

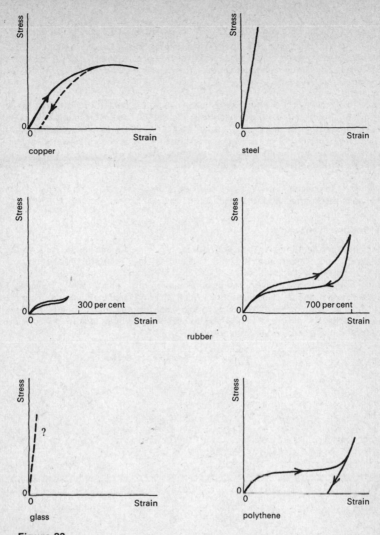

Figure 32
Stress–strain graphs.

Further microscopic interpretation

Having looked at the macroscopic behaviour of materials, we turn again to microscopic interpretations. The calculation of the stiffness of atomic bonds will be used again in work on waves and oscillations (Unit 4) to predict a wave velocity and to consider the absorption of light by a crystal. In later work on ionic crystals (Unit 3), there is a more detailed calculation which relates an elastic modulus to the electrical nature of the bonds in such a crystal.

These moves back and forth from the large to the small scale are part of our attempt to reveal the shape of physics, in which much depends on such interplay. These microscopic calculations should also increase students' ability to handle numbers like 10^{-10}, which they will need to use so often in the future. Having seen how information about structures might be obtained, the material that follows shows how this information might be put to use. This is deliberately simple and limited in scope, intended to be suggestive rather than complete.

Teachers may like to consult Tabor, *Gases, liquids and solids*, page 138, for another version of the relation between the Young modulus and an atomic force constant.

Students' book

Question 32 goes through this argument step by step, so that students can do it themselves, saving laboratory time for more appropriate activities. Question 31 may be useful preparation.

Students will not necessarily be impressed by a calculation of an atomic spring constant. They could feel the stretchiness of the O-level steel springs (item 2A) and estimate their spring constant. It happens to have a similar order of magnitude to that calculated for atomic bonds. A physicist now wants to know why the stiffness of bonds has this size, and it would be a good idea to promise students a further look at the problem later on (Unit 3).

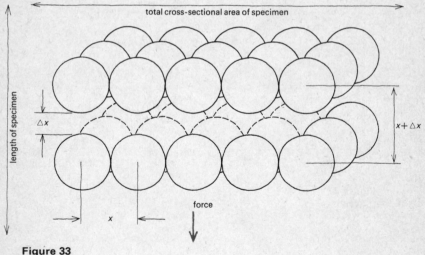

Figure 33
Simplified picture of stretching a metal.

Stretching and breaking 'as the atoms see it'

The materials seen behave differently. Why? What is happening at the atomic level? These questions are now pursued a little.

When steel wire is pulled a little, and then relaxed again, how might the movement of the atoms be imagined? Figure 33 suggests a simplified picture, in which layers of atoms are pulled apart a small extra distance Δx. They are shown in a simple cubic array, with an unstretched spacing x between atoms (not because this is correct for steel but because it is easy to think about).

If the steel is pulled out by 0.1 per cent, by what fraction is the spacing x extended? (The same.)

$$\text{strain} = \frac{\Delta x}{x}$$

Suppose each pair of atoms is pulled together as if there were a spring between them, with a force $k\Delta x$, where k is the stiffness of the interatomic 'spring'.

How is the stress in the specimen calculated? (Force divided by area.) The stress is the force $k\Delta x$ between each pair of atoms multiplied by $1/x^2$, the number of atoms in one square metre cross-section.

$$\text{stress} = k\Delta x \, \frac{1}{x^2}$$

The Young modulus for steel is 20×10^{10} N m^{-2}. The spacing x for steel is 3×10^{-10} m roughly. What is k?

$$\text{The Young modulus} = \frac{\text{stress}}{\text{strain}} = \frac{k}{x} \quad (\Delta x \text{ cancels}).$$

Whence $k = 60$ N m^{-1}.

This brief comparison, strictly limited in scope, is meant to show how microscopic models based on X-ray evidence can help to explain the behaviour of materials. A detailed treatment is not required, and only a few simple points are made. We are not especially concerned with explaining the behaviour of the particular materials chosen (rubber, copper, glass), not, at any rate, with any completeness. The work should rather illustrate how such explanations may be possible.

Students should, after the following work, remember these things. A material like rubber, with elastic strains of several hundred per cent, is unusual. Materials which deform by stretching interatomic bonds (unlike rubber) can only stretch elastically by a small fraction. If, as in copper, there are many regular layers of identical atoms, slip is possible. Slip by means of dislocations is an added possibility. When the structure is a more random but strongly bonded lattice as in glass, slip is less plausible and fracture occurs without it, tending to be initiated by cracks, the cracks being unblunted by slip at their tips.

Slides

1.4 Rubber, unstretched (electron diffraction)

1.5 Rubber, stretched (electron diffraction)

1.9 Water (X-ray diffraction)

Students' book

Question 33 is about rubber.

The rubber molecule

The C—C bond angles are fixed, but rotation can occur about these bonds, so that the chain bends and wriggles randomly. When the rubber is stretched, the chains are straightened, and also tend to line up (figure 34 b).

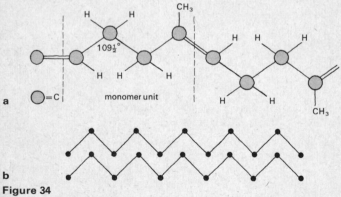

a
Figure 34
a Part of the molecular chain of rubber.
b Crude picture of stretched rubber.

A rough model can be made from 25 mm polystyrene balls (item 1016/1) and cocktail sticks (item 1053) pushed in at about the right angle. Aligned at random, the chain curls up on itself.

Microscopic interpretation of the behaviour of three materials

Rubber

Rubber is peculiar, stretching by several hundred per cent, but returning again when released.

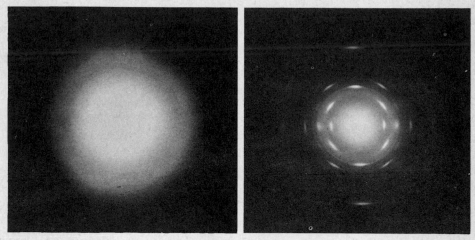

Figure 35
Diffraction pattern formed by (a) unstretched, (b) stretched rubber.
Photographs, (a) Natural Rubber Producers' Association, (b) Professor E. H. Andrews.

Figure 35 *a* is a diffraction photograph of unstretched rubber. There are no sharp spots or rings, that is, there is little regular pattern in the structure. Compare figure 36, an X-ray photograph of water, which one would rightly expect not to be orderly.

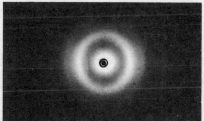

Figure 36
Distilled water (X-ray diffraction).
Photograph, Pilkington Brothers Ltd.

Chemical evidence suggests that rubber molecules are long chains: the class may suggest that when rubber is stretched, a jumbled curled-up set of long chains line up alongside each other. This would explain the existence of spots in the diffraction photograph of stretched rubber (figure 35 *b*), for sharp diffraction spots (or rings) will be expected where there is some orderliness.

Experiments
1.9 Splitting of stretched rubber

Each pair requires:

  1053 50 mm square of balloon rubber

  1053 pin

The squares are cut from toy balloons. The rubber should be stretched as hard as possible in one direction and then pierced. Stirring the pin about gently helps.

It might be helpful to split stretched polythene too; this may need only a fingernail.

Electron diffraction – wave/particle duality

The rubber diffraction photographs were in fact taken with electrons, not with X-rays. The final part of the course will take up this tremendous problem of particles having wave properties. An early mention of these coming studies may help to stimulate interest.

Probable arrangements

The chains of molecules in rubber twist and turn at random, and are most likely to be at some length in between tightly coiled and straightened out. If the point can be made lightly, it makes a useful anticipation of our later concern with a statistical view of the Second Law of Thermodynamics (Unit 9, *Change and chance*). There it is argued that thermal equilibrium is reached because that is the likely thing to happen. The most likely length for a randomly folded chain n units long is of order $\sqrt{n}$ units: compare the random walk from Nuffield O-level Physics *Teachers' guide IV*, page 228 onwards. See Appendix C.

Experiment
1.9　Splitting of stretched rubber

One student stretches a square of thin rubber, while another 'stirs' the middle with a pin. The rubber splits along the stretched direction, supporting the view that molecules have lined up. Well-stretched rubber is stiff (large modulus) because the bonds are then being stretched directly.

Copper

When copper is pulled, what happens after the elastic region? (It yields, or flows.) Metals, unlike rubber or glass, can be hammered flat or drawn through a die to make wires. The X-ray evidence has suggested that copper is made of a regular pattern of identical atoms packed as closely as possible, which suggests that the bonds between atoms in copper amount to a general attraction, with no specific directions being preferred.

How might such a material yield or flow? (Layers could slip.) If a layer slipped, would the structure be spoiled? (Not if it slipped the right way; see figure 37.)

Figure 37
Slipping of regular layers of atoms.

Demonstration and class experiment
1.10 Bubble raft model of dislocations

Each group will need:

1055   Petri dish

1055   length of rubber tubing to fit gas tap

1054   glass tube, 5 mm bore, drawn out to a fine jet
or
1055   hypodermic needle, 25 gauge

L-shaped pieces of wire (about 14 s.w.g.) with rubber tube over the ends

1056   bubble solution: 1 Teepol, 8 glycerol, 32 water, parts by volume

522   Hoffmann clip

Bubbles are blown by connecting the jet to the gas tap as in experiment 1.2. This time the bubbles need to be smaller; a diameter of about one or two millimetres is very satisfactory. For this purpose the jet needs to be very fine indeed (about 0.2 mm diameter) and it is therefore very fragile if made of glass. It takes several minutes for bubbles of this small diameter to make a raft big enough for experimental purposes.

Very rarely will a perfect raft be formed. The dislocations are most easily seen if the raft is viewed almost in line with the surface of the bubbles.

The L-shaped pieces of wire can be used to compress and stretch the raft, causing the dislocations to move. A very small amount of compression is needed and once a dislocation is detected it can be moved backwards and forwards by carefully compressing and stretching the raft. Others may prefer to use shaped metal plates, as in figure 38.

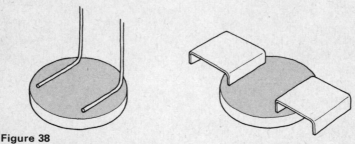

Figure 38
A means of compressing a bubble raft.

A sheet of white paper underneath the tank and perhaps some side illumination may make the effects easier to see in individual experiments. However, by far the best way to view the movement of the bubbles is to project them onto a screen using an overhead projector. The small-sized bubbles are just distinguishable and form a dark surface in which the movement of the dislocations is strikingly obvious.

Demonstration and class experiment
1.10 Bubble raft model of dislocations

If the class is told there is a way for identical layers of atoms to move past each other, without the whole layer moving, they can look for such a thing happening in a bubble raft when it is squeezed between small barriers. (See figure 39 *a*, *b*, *c*, and *d*.)

Students should be able to observe dislocations running along a row of bubbles as the raft is deformed. Since only one atom moves at a time, this kind of slipping may be easier than the slipping of whole layers all together. Dislocations are the main reason for the low yield stress of most pure metals. The possible existence of dislocations makes it the more plausible that a pure metal yields easily.

(To adjust the position of a carpet, a ruck is often formed and kicked across the carpet, thus moving it a few inches. To pull the carpet bodily is very hard.)

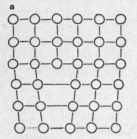 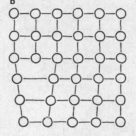 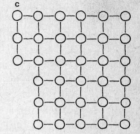

Figure 39
a, b, c Movement of a dislocation.

Further discussion of dislocations

Teachers who wish to go beyond the course material and discuss what effect dislocations have on the strength of materials might consult:

Cottrell, 'The nature of metals' in the *Scientific American* book *Materials.*

Gordon, *The new science of strong materials,* Chapter 4.

Martin, 'New strengths for old metals' in Loftas and Gwynne, *Advances in materials science.*

Moffatt, Pearsall, and Wulff, *The structure and properties of materials,* Volume 1, Chapter 4.

Tabor, *Gases, liquids and solids,* page 161.

Dislocations and defects

Not all defects in a lattice are dislocations, and not all defects make a crystal slip easily. The small size of the crystal grains in a normal metal limits the extent to which dislocations move about, since they stop at crystal boundaries. A cadmium wire, heat-treated to form a single crystal, is dramatically weaker than the polycrystalline material because dislocations can travel more readily.

Foreign atoms introduced into the lattice as in steel may make for greater strength, sometimes by pinning down dislocations. Work hardening functions by generating so many dislocations that they pin each other down. In summary, a perfect lattice would be strong, but a moderate number of dislocations can reduce the strength by a large factor.

Film

Teachers should see the Bragg film 'Bubble model of a metal'.

Aim

To teach adequately about dislocations would take much longer than we can spare. We do not, therefore, expect students to remember the idea in detail. The teaching serves to indicate further uses of microscopic model making, and we hope that students will increasingly seek to use and find out more about such models.

Slides

Slide 1.16 shows grain boundaries in a bubble raft.

Slide 1.17 shows a dislocation in a bubble raft.
It is figure 39*d.*

Students' book

See question 36.

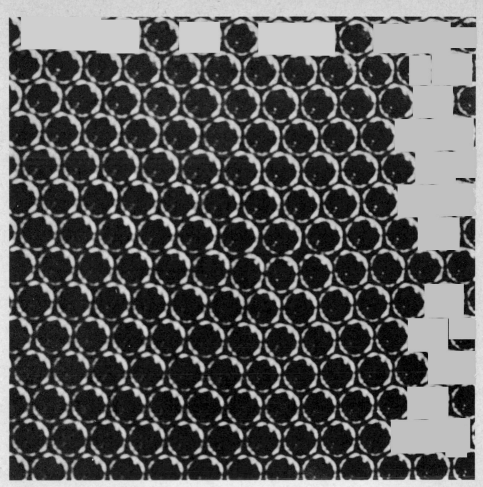

Figure 39 d
Bubble raft model of a dislocation.
Photograph, Sir Lawrence Bragg, F.R.S.

Demonstration
1.11 Cracks and brittle fracture

Required:

508	Bunsen burner
1054	0.1 m length of soda glass rod, about 3 mm diameter *3*
1055	file, e.g. triangular
	matchstick
1053	strip polythene, 100 mm × 10 mm, 250 gauge *2*
529	scissors
1055	safety screen (Perspex)
1083	polarizing filters, 50 mm × 50 mm *2*
	slide projector

1.11a

File a nick across a glass rod, place the rod over a matchstick with the nick uppermost and over the match, and press the ends gently. The rod should snap easily and cleanly. To emphasize the crack-opening action, try two rods together, one with the filed nick on its underside.

1.11b

Put one polaroid in the slide carriage of the projector and place the other over the lens, crossing them. Hold the strip of polythene in the projector, and focus the strip on the screen. Pull the strip. Colours develop over the image as the strip is stressed. Make a cut half way across a second strip, and pull that. Colours develop at the tip of the crack.

Concentration of strain can be shown by ruling a grid on a sheet of rubber, cutting a nick, and stretching it (see figure 40).

Figure 40
Strain concentration due to a nick in a rubber sheet.

A teacher in the trials recommends an acetate strip (item 51F) with a notch in it projected between crossed polaroids.

1.11c

Heat the middle of a rod and pull out a half-metre long fibre. When it is cool, break it nearer to one end, and bend the long fibre into an arc by pressing it on the bench (figure 41). Release it, run the fibre between the fingers, and then try again. This time it snaps. Repeat, with a *new* fibre, touching first the inside and then the outside of the bent glass with another glass fibre. When touched on the outside, the glass snaps at once. The experiment needs practice, and is not too easy.

A safety screen will remove any possibility of students being hit by flying glass, and they can then be grouped around the demonstration.

Glass

Demonstration
1.11 Cracks and brittle fracture

1.11a

How is glass rod cut? (A file mark is made, and the rod bent across the crack.)
Why does this work? Why does the glass snap cleanly? At the bottom of a narrow
crack, the forces are spread over a small area, so the stress is high.

1.11b

Stress concentration may be shown by projecting the image of a nick cut in a strip
of polythene or Sellotape and held between crossed polaroids. A strip without a
nick should be stretched first, to show that stress produces colours. It is hoped that
interested students will be allowed to take polaroid squares home to try this and
other photoelastic effects for themselves.

1.11c

Glass is weak because very small cracks easily form. A freshly made glass fibre will
bend elastically quite a long way (figure 41). With a piece strained as in figure 41,
try touching it first on the inside, then on the outside of the bend with another glass
fibre. On the inside, nothing happens; on the outside the fibre snaps at once. The
inside is compressed and the cracks close up, while the outside is in tension and a
crack propagates through the glass.

As J. E. Gordon (in *The new science of strong materials*, page 98) says, 'The worst
sin in an engineering material is not lack of strength or lack of stiffness, desirable as
these properties are, but lack of toughness, that is to say, lack of resistance to the
propagation of cracks.'

Why does glass crack so easily? Evidence about the structure may help.

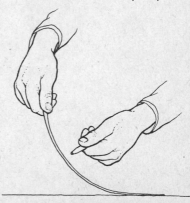

Figure 41
Starting a crack in a stressed glass fibre.

See questions 35–38.

Slides

1.8 X-ray diffraction, glass

1.9 X-ray diffraction, water

1.14 Structure of vitreous silica

The importance of cracks

Cracks are a source of weakness because they increase stresses. The same arguments apply to holes – hatchways in ships, for example. Stress multiplication by 3 mm rivet holes is said to be the reason for the disastrous failures of one of the first commercial jet aircraft, the Comet.

All materials can and do crack, but, if slip can occur to blunt the sharp tip of a crack where stresses are concentrated, the material can withstand deeper cracks without failing.

Gordon, *The new science of strong materials,* Chapter 4, gives a clear account of the problem of cracks.

Ductile and brittle fracture

Two fairly extreme cases have been presented – glass and copper. The former cannot easily slip because it has no long-range order, and so suffers brittle fracture. The latter can slip, and cracks can also be blunted by slip at the tip of the crack which enlarges the area and reduces the stress.

The full story is more complex. If cracks can be prevented, as they can under compression, glass can flow. Rocks in the interior of the Earth flow readily, especially on a long time-scale. Metals can suffer both ductile or brittle failure.

The X-ray diffraction pattern for glass (figure 42) is comparable with that for water (figure 35), both being of the kind obtained when there is little order in the structure (no sharp rings or spots).

Figure 42
X-ray diffraction pattern for glass.
Photograph, Pilkington Brothers Ltd.

Slide 1.14 shows the kind of structure glasses are thought to have. The atoms are arranged in networks based on silicate groups, but with much randomness in the way the networks join up. Glass is rather like a 'solid liquid'. The slow softening rather than sharp melting point may be recalled (experiment 1.7).

Can such a structure slip in the way the regularly arranged copper atoms could? (No, because it lacks the order needed for one bit to slip over and replace another bit.) When such structures break, they come right apart (brittle fracture) rather than slip. But until glass cracks and fractures, it is strong, because it is held together by strong chemical bonds.

New and useful materials

The work of this Unit can now finally come back to the world of useful engineering materials. As well as discussing cracks further, it will be possible to mention some materials at the frontier of present day materials technology.

Talks by students

One of our aims is that students should learn from written sources of information. We suggest, therefore, that some students might be asked to collect information about some materials, particularly concrete, toughened glass, fibreglass, fibre composites, and plywood, and talk about what they have found out. Basing questions on their talks (or on information he gives himself), the teacher can bring out the main issues mentioned on pages 81 and 83.

From a teacher in the trials: '. . . useful, some poor, some missed the point. But worthwhile practice.'

Sources for talks by students

*Frischmann, 'Tall buildings', *Science Journal* reprint.

Gordon, *The new science of strong materials*. See Chapter 6 on wood, Chapter 7 on plywood, and Chapter 8 on fibre reinforced plastics, fibreglass, and reinforced concrete.

*Kennedy, 'High temperature materials', *Science Journal* reprint.

Loftas and Gwynne, *Advances in materials science.* See: Dietz, 'New materials in building' (plastic sandwiches and reinforced concrete); Kelly, 'Composite materials' (fibre reinforcement).

*Morley, 'Fibre reinforced metals', *Science Journal* reprint.

Nuffield Advanced Physics, *Students' book Unit 1*. See Clarke, 'Materials and their uses' and Gunston, 'Carbon fibres'.

Scientific American book *Materials*. See Kelly, 'The nature of composite materials' (laminated steel, boron fibre composite, and fibreglass).

*Reprinted in Nuffield Advanced Physics, *Physics and the engineer*.

Information for teachers

Appendix D contains information about new uses for materials which may help teachers keep their end up in discussion.

1.12 Samples of materials

1.12a Concrete

Ready mixed concrete (item 1053) or, less satisfactory, cement and sand, can be bought in small bags from hardware shops. Bars may be cast in wooden moulds, say $200 \times 50 \times 50$ mm. (Long narrow cardboard boxes will serve.) Reinforcing rods (steel knitting needles, item 1053) may be cast into a bar. The concrete takes at least 24 hours to set.

1.12b Fibreglass

Glass fibre and resin repair kits, intended for car repairs, can be bought from garages. It may be possible to obtain a supply from boating sources, for glass fibre is much used for boat hulls.

1.12c Plywood

Samples of 3 and 5 ply plywoods can easily be bought or obtained from the school workshops. Thin sheets of balsa wood can be glued up into a plywood, laying alternate layers with the grain crossed.

1.12   Samples of composite materials

1.12a   Samples of concrete

Students or teachers may be prepared to cast samples for examination. The brittle fracture should be shown.

Concrete is strong under compression, so that it is much used for pillars. When stretched or bent it snaps easily because, as in glass, cracks develop and propagate. The breaking of china is a similar phenomenon.

Reinforcing rods provide some extra tensile strength. If the reinforcing rods are set in the concrete whilst held in tension, they keep it under compression even when loads are stretching the beam, so that cracks do not propagate. Thus, reinforced concrete combines the cheapness and compressive strength of concrete with the high tensile strength of steel.

Concrete nuclear reactor vessels have been made by building concrete shells with high tensile steel cables embedded in the shell. Reinforced and pre-stressed concrete offer examples of *composite materials*.

Toughened glass

Glass too may be pre-stressed, so that the surface is in compression and cracks will not propagate.

Thermal toughening is achieved by cooling the outside of molten glass by means of jets of air. This causes the outside to cool and contract while the inside is soft and able to give. When, later, the inside hardens and contracts, the outside cannot give and is thus compressed. Looking through a car windscreen while wearing polarizing spectacles it is possible to see the pattern of the air jets used in cooling, because of the in-built strains.

Chemical toughening uses an ion exchange process and replaces the sodium ions in the glass surface with larger potassium ones.

Both these toughening methods increase the strength of glass by a factor of ten. Untreated glass has a strength in the region of 30 to 100 N mm^{-2}.

1.12b   Fibreglass

Fibreglass is a little subtler than reinforced concrete. Glass fibres are strong, but crack easily. If many such fibres in a mat are bonded in a resin which sticks to them, the resulting material has useful properties.

Bridges

The first iron bridge was built by Abraham Darby at Coalbrookdale, Shropshire, in 1775. Cast iron was used, and the bridge still stands. Iron chains were used in a suspension bridge crossing the Tees in 1741. Wrought iron was used by Telford for his suspension bridge crossing the Menai Straits built between 1818 and 1825. Experiments by Hodgkinson and Fairbairn for Stephenson's wrought iron tubular railway bridge over the Menai Straits (built in 1850) revealed the inadequate tensile strength of cast iron compared with wrought iron. Some early iron bridges collapsed, including the Tay bridge in 1879, and in the 1870s and 1880s iron railway truss bridges in America collapsed at the rate of twenty-five a year.

Structural high tensile steel was the material that emerged from these failures, coming into general use after the 1880s. It has made possible many beautiful bridges, particularly those of the suspension type which employ its high tensile strength to advantage.

Students' book

See questions 37 to 44.

Why are materials scientists interested in fibres?

The current interest in fibres springs from the fact that very thin fibres of most materials turn out to have a larger breaking stress than thicker specimens. See Gordon, *The new science of strong materials,* Chapter 3, especially the graph on page 73.

Slides

1.18   pouring concrete

1.19   reinforcing rods in a concrete floor

1.20   reinforced concrete pillar

1.21   pre-stressing a concrete beam

1.22   toughened glass windscreens

Individual fibres will crack, but a crack need not propagate through the material as a whole. The resin yields and distributes the stress among other fibres. The composite has some of the stiffness of the fibres and the toughness of the resin.

There are exciting new developments in the field of fibre composites, especially materials using carbon fibres, or high tensile metal fibres embedded in more ductile metals.

1.12c   Plywood and other sandwich materials

Plywoods with the grains crossed can be surprisingly strong (try splitting a piece in the hands). The advantage of avoiding the tendency of sheets of wood to split along the grain is obvious.

Wood itself is a natural composite, having strong but brittle cellulose fibres embedded in lignin which spreads the stress between fibres.

It is interesting to note that Professor W. O. Alexander claims (*New Scientist* 15 May 1969) that on the basis of cost per unit of strength, wood and concrete are as good as or better than other materials.

Appendices

Appendix A
Metallic crystal structures

Teachers may wish to have further information about the crystal structures common among metals.

Hexagonal close-packed

The repeat unit or 'unit cell' is formed of two of the hexagonal rings of spheres shown in figure 43 separated by the group of three shown in figure 44.

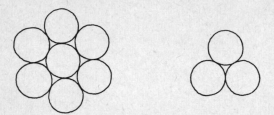

Figures 43 and 44

The complete cell is shown in figure 45.

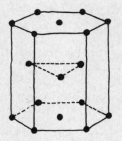

Figure 45

The structure can be built out of planes of hexagonally packed layers, in which alternate layers repeat ABAB.

Face-centred cubic

When the face-centred cubic structure is built from hexagonally packed layers in the repeat pattern ABCABC, the cubic unit cell is situated in the lattice with a diagonal in a vertical position.

The face-centred cubic unit cell can be thought of as built out of hexagonally packed layers by starting with six spheres in a triangular shape (figure 46) with a seventh sphere on top as shown (dotted line). Two of these units placed back to back form the cube.

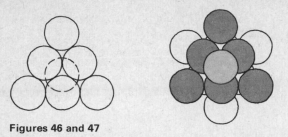

Figures 46 and 47

Figure 47 shows the positions of the spheres in the cube looking down on one corner. This is the way in which it fits into the crystal lattice, standing on one corner with the opposite corner (the middle ball in figure 47) up in the air. If the other spheres are placed round it, the ABCABC stacking becomes apparent.

Body-centred cubic

Both the face-centred cubic and hexagonal close-packed arrangements give a packing density of 74 per cent.

This is the highest possible density, and, of course, corresponds to the closest possible packing for a regular three-dimensional structure. The body-centred cubic structures give the second closest packing (68 per cent). The free construction of this lattice using polyzote spheres is not possible since the spheres tend to run closer together. Each sphere must be fixed as it is placed in position. The basic body-centred unit cell is illustrated in figure 48.

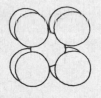

Figure 48

Appendix B
Instructions for building crystal models

Face-centred cubic model (demonstration 1.4)

Two hundred expanded polystyrene balls, each 50 mm in diameter are needed. Glue such as Evo-stik 863 is suitable.

The model is built up of seven layers of balls. In each layer the balls are arranged in hexagonal array, as shown in figure 49. The model is started with a layer which will ultimately be in the middle, and is built outwards. Figure 7 shows the completed model (page 21).

Figure 49 a shows the first layer to be made. It is started by sticking seven balls in a straight line. The balls may be supported by straight edges while the glue dries. Alternatively, a length of V-shaped channel is convenient. To finish this layer, balls are stuck on either side of the row until the layer shown in figure 49 a is complete. When this first layer is dry and firm, the rest of the model is built onto it.

The first layer just made is shown again in figure 49 b, the balls of which it is made being shown this time by circles with tinted outlines. A second layer of balls, shown in figure 49 b by circles with solid outlines, is built upon it. The balls must go exactly in the positions shown. Balls which overhang the edges need temporary support. Each ball should be glued to every ball it touches, throughout the construction.

Later figures, 49 c to g, show the construction of further layers. In each figure, the layer on which the new one is to be placed is shown by tinted circles, while the balls of the new layer are shown with solid outlines.

Figure 49 c shows the positions of balls in a third layer (solid outlines) on top of balls of the second layer (tinted outlined). The third layer balls go over spaces in the first layer, not over balls of the first layer. It is this placing, maintained throughout the model, which makes the structure face-centred cubic rather than hexagonal close-packed.

Figure 49 d shows the fourth layer to be added on top of the third layer, previously shown in figure 49 c. This completes one half of the model.

When this half is firm, it is turned over to rest upon the fourth layer, so that the original layer is uppermost. Turn the model until it is oriented as shown in figure 49 e, which shows balls of the second layer appearing behind some of those of the first layer. Add balls of a fifth layer in positions shown by solid circles in figure 49 e. Overhanging balls again need temporary support.

Two more layers, the sixth and seventh, complete the model. Figure 49 f shows the sixth layer added to the fifth, while figure 49 g shows the seventh layer added to

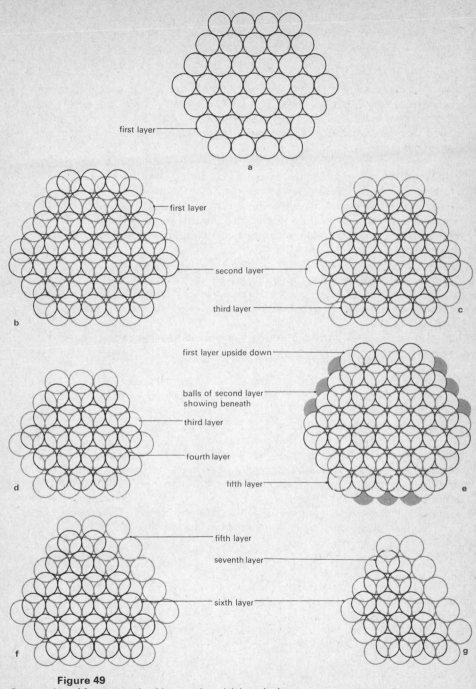

first layer

first layer

second layer

third layer

b

c

first layer upside down

balls of second layer
showing beneath

third layer

fourth layer

d

fifth layer

e

fifth layer

seventh layer

sixth layer

f

g

Figure 49
Construction of face-centred cubic crystal model, layer by layer.

the sixth. Both these layers are left partially incomplete, so as to leave a convenient plane exposed. In use, the model rests upon this exposed plane (as in figure 7, p.21), not upon any of the layers out of which it was built.

Care is needed in building the second half of the model, so that the proper repeat pattern is maintained. Balls in each layer naturally come over gaps in the layer immediately below, but they must also come over gaps in the layer below that. Balls are over balls in every fourth layer, repeating ABCABC. It is essential to observe correctly the orientation shown in figure 49 *e*, when the first half is turned over.

The size of the balls is important. They are chosen to bear the same ratio to the diameter of copper atoms as does the wavelength of microwaves used in the experiment (3 cm) to that of a convenient X-ray source (copper K_α radiation). Then the diffraction angles are identical for the microwave analogue and X-ray diffraction from copper, and the size of a copper atom can be found by direct scaling.

There is some evidence that diffraction effects are poor if much glue fills the space around each joint. The least possible amount of glue should be used. But, as mentioned above, each ball should be stuck to every other ball it touches.

Instructions for making the sodium chloride model

1016/2   expanded polystyrene sphere, 50 mm diameter   *63*

1016/1   expanded polystyrene sphere, 25 mm diameter   *62*

1022   jig for making NaCl model

1053   glue, Evo-stik 863

It is convenient to make the model in the shape of a cube, the edges of which contain five spheres. Figure 50 shows the appearance of the first layer of spheres. The jig holds them in position while the glue is drying.

Figure 51 shows the second layer. Alternate layers of these two kinds are made, until there are five in all. The layers are then glued together.

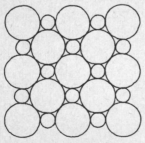 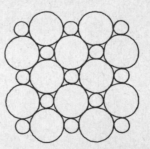

Figures 50 and 51

Appendix C
The stretching of rubber

The following account of the behaviour of rubber may be helpful. The facts (experiment 1.7) are:

a When rapidly stretched, rubber becomes warm.

b When rubber is relaxed under tension it becomes cool.

c If stretched rubber relaxes freely, little temperature change occurs.

Fact **c** indicates that the internal energy of rubber does not depend on the extension (compare an ideal gas). There is little or no energy stored in stretched bonds in extended rubber. When rubber is stretched, the C–C bonds rotate so that polymer chains uncurl. The monomer unit in natural rubber is as in figure 52.

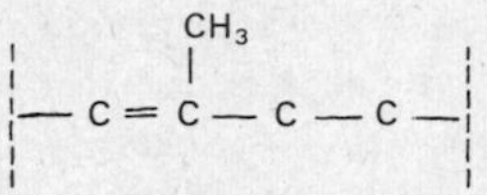

$$-\,C = C - C - C -$$
$$\overset{\displaystyle CH_3}{|}$$

Figure 52

The C–C–C bonds make a fixed angle of $109\tfrac{1}{2}°$. When uncurled, a chain of n monomer units has a length proportional to n. When curled up in a random fashion, the mean distance from beginning to end of the chain is proportional to $\sqrt{n}$ (compare the random walk, Nuffield O-level Physics, *Teachers' guide IV*, pp. 226–42). The ratio of stretched to unstretched length is thus proportional to $\sqrt{n}$, with a constant that is of order unity, so that polymers of hundreds of units can have extensions up to ten times their original length.

One may picture the units of the polymer chains as in continual thermal motion which tends to produce random, coiled-up configurations. Thus, if stretched rubber is warmed, it either contracts (chains coil more) or exerts a larger tension (chains try to coil up more). As fact **c** indicates, the force exerted by stretched rubber is not the result of stretched bonds, but is a consequence of thermal agitation trying to make the chains more randomly arranged and hence shorter overall.

Fact **a** is a consequence of the mechanical energy transferred to the rubber when it is stretched, which is not stored in stretched bonds but in increased thermal agitation. There is a parallel with the compression of an ideal gas, where all the energy delivered in compression goes into thermal motion, there being no interaction between molecules. Fact **b** is the reverse of **a**.

Thermodynamically, when rubber is stretched the number of chain configurations falls, and the configurational entropy of the rubber falls. The entropy rise, needed so that the total entropy does not fall, occurs in the thermal entropy of the warmer rubber or its surroundings.

Appendix D
Applications supplement: new uses for new materials

This Appendix is a sample of the kind of material to which teachers can add from their own reading, which could be used to increase the range and interest of discussions of applications of physics.

> 'Nineteenth-century science enabled us to design strong engineering structures such as bridges, boilers, and dams. Twentieth-century science is enabling us to design the materials of construction themselves, such as super-alloys, new ceramics, and fibre reinforced composites. Engineering materials are no longer regarded as unfathomable "black boxes" with immutable properties; we can probe into them, both experimentally, using such tools as X-ray diffraction analysis and electron microscopy, and also theoretically, using such tools as atomic theory and statistical thermodynamics, to find out how their atoms are packed together, how these packings determine the bulk properties of the material, and how to produce those packings that give the best properties. All this has transformed the subject known as "strength of materials", once a branch of classical mechanics concerned with the design of engineering structures, into a modern applied science in which atomic physics, molecular chemistry, and physical metallurgy join forces with engineering and economics for designing strong materials according to clear scientific principles.'
> *From Cottrell, A. H. (1968) Foreword to* Strength of materials.
> (*A* Contemporary Physics *reprint.*) *Taylor and Francis.*

In any branch of technology, progress depends upon the availability of the right material for the job in hand, but what is the right material for a rocket nose cone, a fuel canning tube in a nuclear reactor, or an artificial heart valve?

The search for new materials has long since gone beyond the properties of the solid elements of the Periodic Table. Even within the field of metals, elements which were laboratory curiosities twenty years ago are now almost commonplace as constructional materials. Table 1 gives some examples.

Metal	Properties	Applications
Titanium	Low density (4.5×10^3 kg m^{-3}). Readily alloyed to give very high strength at room temperature and good creep-resistance (i.e. resistance to gradual permanent deformation which develops under load) up to 500 °C. Extremely corrosion resistant.	Aircraft and aero engine components. Chemical plant components exposed to high temperatures and corrosive environments. Marine components. Surgical implants.
Beryllium	Very low density (1.85×10^3 kg m^{-3}). Exceptionally high modulus of elasticity. The value for beryllium is 303×10^9 N m^{-2} compared to 207×10^9 N m^{-2} for steel. Very low neutron absorption. Excellent thermal conductivity. Higher specific heat than any other structural metal.	Fuel canning tubes in gas-cooled reactors. Windows in X-ray tubes. Applications requiring a heat-sink to absorb sudden thermal loads, e.g. atmospheric re-entry of space vehicle. Parts of airframes where thermal gradients occur in high speed aircraft. Inertial guidance gyroscopic devices.
Niobium	High melting point (2470 °C). Strength maintained up to high temperatures (1200 °C). High ductility, i.e. easily pulled out into wires. Medium to low neutron-absorption characteristics. Good corrosion resistance.	Fuel canning tubes and accessories in liquid-metal cooled fast-breeder reactors. Components for high temperature applications, e.g. thermocouple sheaths. Base material for alloys designed for service requiring strength at high temperatures, e.g. gas turbine blades. In alloy form for super-conducting solenoids, magnets, and power transformers capable of operating at high field strengths (10 T).
Tantalum	High melting point (3000 °C). High resistance to corrosion by acids. High ductility. Forms an anodic film of high chemical and electrical stability.	Construction of chemical plant components. Valves and capacitors. Possible base for high temperature alloys.

Table 1

Aerospace engineering

The requirements for materials in this field are for high strength and stiffness with as low a weight as possible. In addition, extreme temperature environments are encountered, for example, in gas turbine engines, rocket motors, supersonic flight, and cryogenic fuel storage systems (see figure 53).

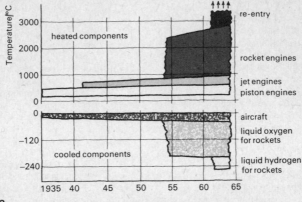

Figure 53
Temperature environments encountered by aerospace vehicles.
From Fishlock, D. (1967) The new materials, *Murray. (Courtesy, NASA.)*

Materials able to retain their mechanical properties under such conditions are needed. The operating temperatures of gas turbine blades approach 1000 °C in civil aircraft and are higher still in military engines. Under typical conditions of service the thrust from a gas turbine can be doubled for a 200 °C increase in its working temperature. Turbine blades need to be made from materials capable of retaining their strength and stiffness at almost white heat whilst being simultaneously subjected to severe mechanical stress and a corrosive atmosphere.

Blade failures bedevilled the work of pioneers in the gas turbine field and led Sir Frank Whittle to remark that '. . . in the early days of blade failures the engineers did more running than the engines.' Today, blades are made from nickel-based alloys such as the Nimonic range. These are complex mixtures containing some six elements; cobalt, molybdenum, and tungsten stiffen the basic matrix of nickel-chromium alloy, and heat treatment introduces fine particles of nickel-aluminium or nickel-titanium compounds.

As they are normally produced, metals are polycrystalline and are both harder and stronger than imperfect single crystals. This is because dislocation movements, or slip, occur in the individual crystals whose slip planes are randomly orientated with respect to one another. On reaching the boundary between one crystal and another, slip is arrested and does not always propagate across the grain boundary. Thus grain size is an important factor in strengthening metals, fine grain structure introducing many grain boundaries which block dislocations. The effect of grain size on the hardness of aluminium brass is shown in figure 54, whilst for pure copper, a reduction in grain size to 10 μm increases the strength by 2×10^8 N m^{-2}.

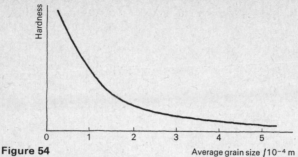

Figure 54
Average grain size $/10^{-4}$ m
Effect of grain size on hardness of an aluminium brass.

In alloys foreign atoms are introduced to interfere with the movement of dislocations. At room temperatures and above, clusters of between 10^9 and 10^{12} foreign atoms are very effective and such clusters are formed by making a supersaturated solution at high temperature, quenching, and then heating at low temperature to allow precipitation of the clusters to take place. This technique, known as age hardening, is used to strengthen aluminium alloys; that used for the airframe of Concorde is made in this way, an intermetallic compound $CuMgAl_2$ being precipitated.

Plastics as constructional materials

Plastics can, surprisingly, find uses in engines, where they are used together with glass or carbon fibres forming composite materials which are both stiff and light. The advantages of lightening engines by the use of such materials can be illustrated by considering the Rolls-Royce Conway engine which powers the V.C. 10 airliner. The engine, mass 2268 kg, provides a thrust of over four times its weight. If the mass of each engine could be trimmed by only 68.0 kg, a four-engined aircraft could carry an additional three passengers, which would increase its earnings sufficiently to almost double the operators' profit! Most of the passenger pay load in an aircraft simply covers the operating costs; it is only the last few people who represent clear profit. Consequently a small increase in the total passengers carried can make a significant improvement. Rolls-Royce are using glass fibre reinforced plastics in the construction of gas turbines to provide lift for vertical take-off aircraft. Once the aircraft is airborne, the lift engines become so much dead weight which must be kept as low as possible. Thrust to weight ratios of about 16:1 have been achieved with such engines, as compared to less than 5:1 for conventional gas turbines.

Glass fibre reinforced plastics are used to fabricate radomes for aircraft. In the
military field, high speed attack aircraft, such as the Lightning, require
forward-looking radar to be carried in the nose and the equipment is housed in a
fibreglass plastic nose cone, the radome (see also the nose cone of Concorde in
figure 58). A metal casing (unlike the plastic one) would not transmit the radar
waves.

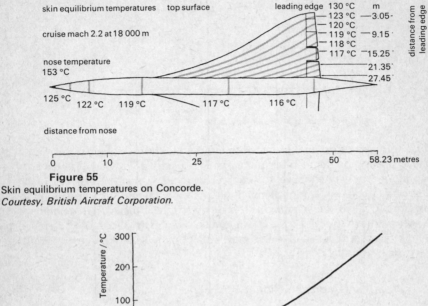

Figure 55
Skin equilibrium temperatures on Concorde.
Courtesy, British Aircraft Corporation.

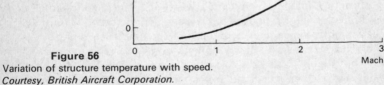

Figure 56
Variation of structure temperature with speed.
Courtesy, British Aircraft Corporation.

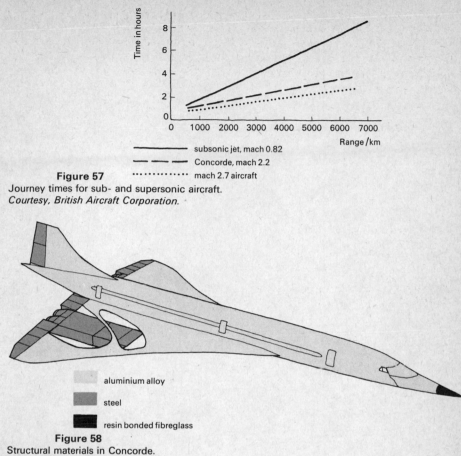

Figure 57
Journey times for sub- and supersonic aircraft.
Courtesy, British Aircraft Corporation.

subsonic jet, mach 0.82
Concorde, mach 2.2
mach 2.7 aircraft

aluminium alloy

steel

resin bonded fibreglass

Figure 58
Structural materials in Concorde.
Courtesy, British Aircraft Corporation.

Lists of films, loops, slides, books, and apparatus

Films and film loops

16 mm film

'Bubble model of a metal' (optional), 16 minutes, black and white, sound. British Film Institute, 42–43 Lower Marsh, London S.E.1.

8 mm film loops

'The diffraction of X-rays by a crystal.' Longman Chemistry Loop 582 37206 2 (optional).

'Bragg reflection of waves.' Ealing Scientific, Standard 8, 80–2363/2, Super 8, 80–2363/1 (optional).

The following series of four loops was made in conjunction with the Nuffield Advanced Physics Project.

'X-ray diffraction 1 Production of the X-ray beam.' Penguin. XX1663.

'X-ray diffraction 2 Diffraction of monochromatic X-rays by a single crystal.' Penguin. XX1664.

'X-ray diffraction 3 Diffraction of monochromatic X-rays by a powder specimen.' Penguin. XX1665.

'X-ray diffraction 4 Determination of the wavelength of X-rays using a diffraction grating.' Penguin. XX1666.

Slides

Slide 1.1

A diagram to illustrate the arrangement used in an X-ray powder camera.
The strip of film is fixed round the inside of the camera which is in fact just a metal cylinder. If the camera radius is known, the Bragg angle for each cone of X-rays can be found after measuring the circumferential separation of the two lines corresponding to the intercepts of each X-ray cone at the film.

Slide 1.2

An X-ray powder photograph for copper.
A scale, camera radius, and X-ray wavelength are shown so that students may determine Bragg angles and lattice spacings. The pip on the upper edge of the photograph — by chance it comes at line 4 — is simply for identifying the left- and righthand sides of the photograph, which may be necessary, for example, in tracking down operating faults.

Data
Camera radius 45.0 mm.

Line	Indices	Bragg angle
1	111	21.7°
2	200	25.3°
3	220	37.1°
4	311	45.0°
5 (weak)	222	47.6°
6	400	58.6°
7	331	68.4°
8	420	72.5°

Wavelength — Copper $K_\alpha = 0.154\,18$ nm (weighted mean of K_{α_1}, K_{α_2}). At high angles, the K_{α_1} and K_{α_2} lines may be resolved.
Table 2

Slide 1.3

An X-ray powder photograph for sodium chloride.
The camera radius and X-ray wavelength are the same as for slide 1.2.
The second line (the first is weak) at 15.9° corresponds to the planes whose spacing is equal to the distance between nearest neighbour Na^+ and Cl^- ions.

Slide 1.4

An electron diffraction pattern for unstretched natural rubber, showing only amorphous haloes.
Photograph, Natural Rubber Producers' Research Association.

Slides

Slide 1.1

A diagram to illustrate the arrangement used in an X-ray powder camera.
The strip of film is fixed round the inside of the camera which is in fact just a metal cylinder. If the camera radius is known, the Bragg angle for each cone of X-rays can be found after measuring the circumferential separation of the two lines corresponding to the intercepts of each X-ray cone at the film.

Slide 1.2

An X-ray powder photograph for copper.
A scale, camera radius, and X-ray wavelength are shown so that students may determine Bragg angles and lattice spacings. The pip on the upper edge of the photograph – by chance it comes at line 4 – is simply for identifying the left- and righthand sides of the photograph, which may be necessary, for example, in tracking down operating faults.

Data
Camera radius 45.0 mm.

Line	Indices	Bragg angle
1	111	21.7°
2	200	25.3°
3	220	37.1°
4	311	45.0°
5 (weak)	222	47.6°
6	400	58.6°
7	331	68.4°
8	420	72.5°

Wavelength – Copper $K_\alpha = 0.154\,18$ nm (weighted mean of K_{α_1}, K_{α_2}). At high angles, the K_{α_1} and K_{α_2} lines may be resolved.
Table 2

Slide 1.3

An X-ray powder photograph for sodium chloride.
The camera radius and X-ray wavelength are the same as for slide 1.2.
The second line (the first is weak) at 15.9° corresponds to the planes whose spacing is equal to the distance between nearest neighbour Na^+ and Cl^- ions.

Slide 1.4

An electron diffraction pattern for unstretched natural rubber, showing only amorphous haloes.
Photograph, Natural Rubber Producers' Research Association.

Slide 1.5

An electron diffraction pattern for highly stretched natural rubber, showing evidence of crystallization.
Photograph, Professor E. H. Andrews.

Slide 1.6

An X-ray diffraction pattern for undrawn low density polythene.
Photograph, I.C.I. Plastics Division.

Slide 1.7

An X-ray diffraction pattern for drawn low density polythene (fibre photograph).
Photograph, I.C.I. Plastics Division.

Slide 1.8

An X-ray diffraction pattern for glass.
An annealed Pyrex rod, 0.67 mm in diameter, was placed with its axis perpendicular to a Cu K_α X-ray beam.
Photograph, Pilkington Brothers Ltd.

Slide 1.9

An X-ray diffraction pattern for distilled water.
Details as for slide 1.8 except that the water was contained in a 0.5 mm tube.
Photograph, Pilkington Brothers Ltd.

Slide 1.10

Laue pattern.
An intermetallic compound of aluminium, iron, and silicon in the form of a single crystal.

Slide 1.11

An X-ray diffraction pattern made from a single crystal of haemoglobin that was rotated during the photographic exposure.
Electrons grouped around the centres of the atoms in the crystal scatter the incident X-rays, producing a symmetrical array of spots. Spots that are equidistant from the centre and opposite each other have the same density.
Photograph, Professor M. F. Perutz.

Slide 1.12

The structure of $TlAlF_4$ shown in a drawing.
All four equatorial F atoms of each octahedron are shared, giving layers of composition AlF_4.
*Drawing after Brosset, C. (1937) Z. Anorg. Chem. **235**, 139.*

Slide 1.13

The structure of *p*-diphenylbenzene.

Slide 1.14

The structure of vitreous silica.
SiO_2 occurs in crystalline form as quartz, having a regular crystal structure of silica tetrahedra. The basic structure of the glassy form is the same as crystalline quartz but the bond angles between the oxygen atoms may vary. This gives a complex random network which is typical of the structure of any glass. By adding further oxides the network is modified and even more complex structural arrangements result.
Photograph, Crown Copyright, Science Museum, London.

Slide 1.15

The structure of the lysozyme molecule, shown in a colour photograph of a model.
Photograph, Professor D. C. Phillips, F.R.S.

Slide 1.16

A bubble raft showing grain boundaries.
*Photographed from Proc. Roy. Soc. A, **190**, 1947, with the permission of the Royal Society and by courtesy of Sir Lawrence Bragg, F.R.S.*

Slide 1.17

A bubble raft showing a dislocation.
To locate the dislocation, look diagonally across the picture, close to its plane.
Photograph, Sir Lawrence Bragg, F.R.S.

Slide 1.18

Pouring ready mixed concrete.
This slide, together with slides 1.19, 1.20, and 1.21 may be used to illustrate a common composite material.
Photograph, Cement and Concrete Association.

Slide 1.19

Reinforcing rods in a concrete floor.
Photograph, Cement and Concrete Association.

Slide 1.20

Reinforcing rods in a concrete pillar.
Photograph, Cement and Concrete Association.

Slide 1.21

Manufacture of pre-stressed concrete beams.
In this post-tensioned unit each strand is being stressed separately by a
hydraulically operated jack.
Photograph, Cement and Concrete Association.

Slide 1.22

Toughened glass windscreens: (a) Zebrazone glass, (b) Widezone glass.
Photographs, Triplex Safety Glass Co. Ltd.

Books and further reading

Page numbers of references in this *Guide* appear in bold type.

For students

Strongly recommended for background reading

Bragg, Sir L. (1968) 'X-ray crystallography.' *Scientific American* Offprint No. 325. **26, 46**
Gordon, J. E. (1968) *The new science of strong materials*. Penguin. **10, 60, 74, 78, 80, 82**
Scientific American (1967) *Materials*. W. H. Freeman. **34, 60, 74, 80**

Textbooks for reference

Arons, A. B. (1965) *Development of concepts of physics*. Addison-Wesley. **44**
Baez, A. V. (1967) *The new college physics: a spiral approach*. W. H. Freeman. **44**
Bennet, G. A. G. (1968) *Electricity and modern physics*. (MKS version.) Arnold. **44**
Caro, D. E., McDonell, J. A., and Spicer, B. M. (1962) *Modern physics*. Arnold. **44**
PSSC (1965) *Physics*. 2nd edition. Heath. **44**
PSSC (1968) *College physics*. Raytheon.
Rogers, E. M. (1960) *Physics for the inquiring mind*. Oxford University Press. **44, 50**
Nuffield Advanced Chemistry (1972) *Amount of substance*. Penguin. **14**

Further reading

Bragg, Sir L. (1967) Nuffield O-level Chemistry Background Book *The start of X-ray analysis*.
Longman/Penguin. **26**
Fishlock, D. (1967) *The new materials*. Murray. **94**
*Frischmann, W. W. (1965) 'Tall buildings.' *Science Journal* reprint. **80**
Holden, A., and Singer, P. (1961) *Crystals and crystal growing*. Heinemann.
*Kennedy, A. J. (1965) 'High temperature materials.' *Science Journal* reprint. **80**
Loftas, A. A., and Gwynne, P. (1967) *Advances in materials science*. London University Press.
10, 74, 80
*Morley, J. G. (1966) 'Fibre reinforced metals.' *Science Journal* reprint. **80**
Platts, C. V. (1967) Nuffield O-level Chemistry Background Book *The structure of substances*.
Longman/Penguin. **34**
Walker, O. J. (1967) Nuffield O-level Chemistry Background Book *Plastics*. Longman/Penguin.

For teachers or library

Moffatt, W. G., Pearsall, G. W., and Wulff, J. (1964) *The structure and properties of materials*, Vol 1
Structure. Wiley. (Useful illustrations.) **34, 74**
Nuffield Advanced Chemistry (1070) *Teachers' guide I*. Penguin. (Topics 1, 3, and 8.) **40**
Nuffield O-level Physics (1966) *Teachers' guide III*. Longman/Penguin. **50**
Nuffield O-level Physics (1967) *Teachers' guide V*. Longman/Penguin. **50**
Street, A., and Alexander, W. (1963) *Metals in the service of man*. 4th edition. Penguin.
Tabor, D. (1969) *Gases, liquids and solids*. Penguin. **66, 74**

Theories and models

Bondi, H. (1962) *The Universe at large*. Heinemann. **50**
Bronowski, J. (1960) *The common sense of science*. Penguin. **50**
Dirac, P. A. M. (1963) 'The evolution of the physicist's picture of nature.' *Scientific American*
Offprint No. 292. **50**
Popper, K. R. (1963) *Conjectures and refutations*. Routledge & Kegan Paul. **50**
Watson, J. D. (1968) *The double helix*. Weidenfeld & Nicolson. **50**

Science Journal reprints are no longer available. The above articles will, however, be included in a
collection entitled *Physics and the engineer* to be published in 1972 as part of the Nuffield
Advanced Physics publications.

Apparatus

2B	reel of 32 s.w.g. bare copper wire	1.1, 1.7
4A	drinking straw	optional experiment
23	microscope	1.7
31/2	weight hangers with slotted weights (0.1 kg)	1.7, 1.8
32	1 kg weights	1.7, 1.8
35	S-hooks	1.7
40	single pulley on clamp	1.7, 1.8
44/2	G-clamps, small	1.7
59	l.t. variable voltage supply	1.4, 1.6
64	oscilloscope	1.4
81	newton spring balance (10 N)	1.7, 1.8
90A	ripple tank without legs	1.2
100/1	rectangular plastic tanks	1.2
181	general purpose amplifier	1.4, 1.5, 1.6
183	loudspeaker	1.4, 1.5, 1.6
184/1	3 cm wave transmitter	1.4, 1.5, 1.6
184/2	3 cm wave receiver	1.4, 1.5, 1.6
501	metre rules	1.8
503–6	retort stand base, rod, boss, and clamp	1.7
508	Bunsen burners	1.7, 1.11
522	Hoffman clips	1.2, 1.10
529	scissors	1.7, 1.11
530	pliers	1.7
533	plastic bucket	1.8
1014	wax lens	1.4, 1.5, 1.6
1015	turntable for 3 cm X-ray diffraction analogue	1.4, 1.6
1016/1	expanded polystyrene spheres, 25 mm diameter	see Appendix B
1016/2	expanded polystyrene spheres, 50 mm diameter	1.3, 1.4, 1.6, see Appendix B
1021	aerosol freezer	optional experiment
1022	jig for making NaCl lattice model	see Appendix B
1053	*Local purchase items:*	
	glass wool (e.g. roof insulation)	1.1
	glass fabric (e.g. for curtains)	1.1
	nylon fishing line	1.1
	plywood, 3-ply	1.1, 1.12
	plywood, 5-ply	1.1, 1.12
	fibreglass	1.1
	cocktail sticks	optional experiment
	polythene sheet (e.g. foodbags)	1.1
	polythene sheet (e.g. for gardening)	1.1, 1.7, 1.11
	plastics sample (e.g. lunch box)	1.1
	mixed cement and aggregate	1.1, 1.12
	wood, soft	1.1

wood, hard		1.1
corrugated paper		1.1
metal screen, about 0.3 m square		1.4, 1.5, 1.6
glue, e.g. Evo-stik		1.6, Appendix B
PVC insulating tape		1.7
rubber bands, 50–100 mm long, various thicknesses		1.1, 1.7, optional experiment
thin string		1.7
razor blades		1.7
Sellotape		1.8
rubber balloons		1.9
matches		1.11
steel knitting needles		1.12
hardboard reflector, about 0.3 m square		1.5
expanded polystyrene sheet, 0.3 m square (e.g. ceiling tiles)		1.6
potatoes		optional experiment
silicone putty		optional experiment
sewing needle		optional experiment
pins		1.9
glass fibre and resin repair kit		1.12

1054 *Expendable items:*

glass rod, about 3 mm diameter	1.1, 1.7, 1.11
glass tube, 4–5 mm diameter	1.2, 1.10
stainless steel wire, 44 s.w.g. (item 7A may serve)	1.1, 1.7

1055 *Small laboratory items:*

rubber tubing to fit gas taps	1.2, 1.8, 1.10
hypodermic needle, 25 gauge	1.2, 1.10
Petri dishes	1.10
file, triangular	1.11
Perspex safety screen	1.11
hammer	optional experiment
micrometer screw gauge	1.7, 1.8
Vernier callipers	1.7

1056 *Chemicals:*

Teepol	1.2, 1.10
glycerol	1.2, 1.10
1083 polarizing filters	1.11

Index

Where significant information is contained in an illustration or diagram, the page reference is italicized. In general, odd-numbered page references are to the main text, and even-numbered references are to commentary material.